McGraw-Hill Science

Grade 6

Preparation and Practice for the

ITBS • Stanford 9 • TerraNova

This booklet was written by The Princeton Review, the nation's leader in test preparation. The Princeton Review helps millions of students every year prepare for standardized assessments of all kinds. Through its association with McGraw-Hill, The Princeton Review offers the best way to help students excel on the ITBS®, Stanford 9, and TerraNova®

The Princeton Review is not affiliated with Princeton University or Educational Testing Service.

The Iowa Test of Basic Skills® is a trademark of Riverside Publishing Company. This book has been neither authorized or endorsed by Riverside Publishing Company.

The Stanford 9 is produced by Harcourt Brace & Company. This book has been neither authorized or endorsed by Harcourt Brace & Company.

The TerraNova® is a trademark of CTB/McGraw-Hill. This book has been neither authorized or endorsed by CTB/McGraw-Hill.

Macmillan/McGraw-Hill

A Division of The McGraw-Hill Companies

Macmillan/McGraw-Hill
Two Penn Plaza
New York, New York 10121-2298

Printed in the United States of America
ISBN 0-02-280245-2/6
3 4 5 6 7 8 9 024 07 06 05 04 03

TABLE OF CONTENTS

ABOUT THIS BOOK

This book has three distinct sections. Each section covers one major standardized science test: the Iowa Test of Basic Skills®, the Stanford Achievement Test, or the TerraNova®.

Your students will probably take only one of these three standardized tests. We have marked each section of the book with the name of the test that it covers, so you can easily find and use the section most relevant to you.

If your students will take the Iowa Test of Basic Skills (also known as the ITBS), turn to the pages with the bar along the upper right-hand side that looks like this:

ITBS

If your students will take the Stanford Achievement Test (also known as the Stanford 9 or the SAT-9), turn to the pages with the bar along the middle right-hand side that looks like this:

Stanford 9

If your students will take the TerraNova (sometimes known as the CTBS-5), turn to the pages with the bar along the lower right-hand side that looks like this:

TerraNova

Once you have turned to the section covering the standardized test your students must take, you will see that there are seven unit tests. Each unit test corresponds to one unit in the Grade 6 McGraw-Hill Science textbook.

HOW TO USE THIS BOOK

As students finish each unit in the McGraw-Hill Science textbook, they should complete the corresponding unit test in this workbook. The questions in the unit tests do the following:

- They test the skills and facts covered in each unit of the McGraw-Hill Science textbook.
- They do so in the styles and formats of the science questions on the ITBS, SAT-9, and TerraNova.

Taking these unit tests will help students review the science facts and skills they've learned in class and familiarize them with the types of questions they will see on their standardized test.

Because the unit tests in this workbook are short, we recommend that you use them in addition to other end-of-unit assessments.

We recommend that you photocopy each four-page unit test to hand out at the end of each textbook unit. You may want to allow students to complete the unit tests in a variety of ways. Some suggestions are on the following page.

HOW CAN THIS BOOK HELP MY STUDENTS ON STANDARDIZED TESTS?

This book will help your students become accustomed to answering multiple-choice questions like the ones the ITBS, SAT-9, and TerraNova. Students should learn to use test-taking strategies to answer these types of questions. Many standardized science questions allow students to eliminate answer choices by carefully reading the information presented and using general science concepts, rather than requiring students to remember specific details from science class.

Some students may already be aware of test-taking strategies and employ them; other students may benefit from direct instruction and from seeing and hearing how test-savvy students answer questions. In order to allow students to develop their test-taking skills, we recommend that you begin the year by using the unit tests in a **class or small group activity.** When students show that they have learned and can apply test-taking strategies to questions, have them start to **work on unit tests individually**. Finally, by the end of the year, require all students to take a unit test as a **short practice test** in a test-like environment. The following suggestions can help you structure these methods of using the unit tests.

Class Activity

Distribute a unit test and have students answer the questions as a class. Use the following suggestions to introduce and reinforce test-taking skills.

- Read the first question aloud. Encourage one student to tell you one answer choice that is **not** the right answer. Then ask another student for a second **wrong** answer. Ask a third student to tell you the third **wrong** answer. Finally, ask a fourth student to tell you which answer is left over, and therefore the best answer.
- Explain to students that this strategy can help them when they do not know the answer to a question right away. This process-of-elimination activity is useful for the most difficult questions, and can be used for reviewing unit tests that students took individually, as well.
- Use the chalkboard to help students visualize the process of elimination. Write the answer choice letters on the board, and cross them out as students eliminate them. Don't let students become reliant on crossing out choices on their own papers, though—they sometimes cannot write in standardized test booklets, so they will not be able to cross out eliminated choices during the real test.
- Emphasize using the process of elimination throughout your class discussions of how to answer the unit test questions. Students may be familiar with the process of elimination, but found it only minimally helpful in previous grades. Now, many questions will be difficult enough that only elimination can help students narrow their choices.
- Ask students why they think an answer choice is wrong before allowing them to eliminate it. Students should always be able to justify eliminating a choice with the information presented in the question or their own knowledge of science.

- Give oral feedback to students on their strategies and reasons for eliminating or choosing answers. Help them understand which reasons for eliminating an answer are valid, and which are invalid.
- Discuss what mistakes students might make that would lead them to choose a wrong answer. This is particularly helpful for questions involving a graphic or mathematics. The wrong answer choices are often the results of common student errors, such as overlooking an important word in the question or misinterpreting a graph.

Small Group Activity

- Divide students into groups of two to four. Encourage them to work together to solve problems and answer questions.
- Be sure that students approach the questions with test-taking strategies. Remind them of how to use the process of elimination.
- If you know which students are the better test-takers, spread them throughout the groups. Students who are not sophisticated test-takers may benefit from hearing how a good test-taker decided which answer to choose.

Individual Classwork or Homework

- Students should be able to answer the questions without referring to their textbooks, but you may choose to allow them to use the textbooks in some cases.
- You may want to ask students to show you how they eliminated answers by crossing out choices on their unit tests. However, don't let them become reliant on doing this if they cannot write on their test booklets during the actual administration of the ITBS, SAT-9, or TerraNova.

Short Practice Test

- Separate student desks and arrange the classroom as it will be for the actual standardized exam.
- If students will use a separate answer sheet for the real exam, photocopy and distribute the answer sheet on page 14, 54, or 94.
- Estimate how much time students should be allowed for the number of items in the unit test (based on the time allowed for the real test, which is given in the "What Do I Need to Know..." introduction in each section of this book).
- Tell students that they are taking a short practice test, and ask them to remove everything from their desks except a pencil. They may not speak to their classmates until the practice test is over.
- If students will not be able to write on the test booklets during the real administration, then tell them they cannot do so for the practice test, either. If students must use a separate answer sheet during the real administration, then have them do so now.

- Time students, and keep the classroom atmosphere as much like a real standardized test administration as possible. Minimize distractions and discourage talking. Do not help students answer questions.
- Keep in mind that one unit test does not cover the same breadth of scope that a standardized test does. We do not recommend trying to gauge how well students will do on the real test based on one unit test. The purpose of using a unit test as a short practice test is to accustom students to the conditions under which they will take the real test.

The Benefits to Your Students of Using This Book as Recommended

- Students become familiar with the types of questions they will find on the ITBS, SAT-9, or TerraNova.
- Students have a chance to learn test-taking strategies and practice them.
- Students become comfortable in test-taking environments like those imposed during standardized test administrations.
- Students reinforce their knowledge of material covered in the McGraw-Hill Science textbook.

ITBS

ITBS
ITBS
ITBS

WHAT DO I NEED TO KNOW ABOUT THE ITBS SCIENCE SECTION?

The Iowa Test of Basic Skills covers many other subjects besides science. Your students will probably also take the language arts, mathematics, and social studies sections of the ITBS. This workbook prepares your students for the types of *science* questions they will see on the ITBS.

In the sixth grade, students usually take Level 12 of the ITBS. They must take the Complete Battery version in order to have a science section. Ask your school's test coordinator or principal to find out if your students will take the Complete Battery. Also check to be sure they will take Level 12.

If students take Level 12, they will have 42 science questions to answer in 30 minutes. These numbers are based on Form M, and other forms may vary slightly.

The ITBS is a norm-referenced test, which means that it can be used to compare one group of students to another. On each student's score report there will be a percentile score that shows how she has performed compared to other students at the same grade level. However, technically, the student is not being compared to *all* students at that grade level across the country. She is only compared to the group of students that was in the norm group—a group that *represents* all students at that grade level across the country.

Because the ITBS is a national test, its science questions are not based on any one state or district's science curriculum. Unfortunately, the ITBS does ask questions that require students to know specific science facts and theories—much more so than the TerraNova or SAT-9. This means that the ITBS may contain questions based on concepts that your class did not emphasize.

It is important to do a thorough review of areas covered throughout the year before students take the ITBS. It is also crucial that your students use the process of elimination throughout the test in order to get credit wherever possible for what they know. Because it is a norm-referenced test, the ITBS is designed so that the large majority of students cannot answer every question correctly. "Partial knowledge" can help them eliminate one, two, or three choices, and they should always pick an answer once they've done so.

The list of "content classifications" on page 11 shows the broad areas of science knowledge that are covered on the ITBS.

ITBS Science Content Classifications for Grade 6

Each objective is followed by the code used in the answer key to indicate which questions in the unit tests are associated with it.

Nature of Science (Science-01)

These questions test students' familiarity with the processes of scientific investigation. They require students to be familiar with the common purposes and methods of scientific experiments. Students must explain why certain items are used in an experiment, or what the result of an experiment could be.

Life Science (Science-02)

These questions deal with living organisms and ecosystems. Students must be able to answer questions about common functions of various parts of plants and animals, and have basic knowledge of their interactions.

Earth and Space Sciences (Science-03)

These questions focus on students' knowledge of Earth, Sun, and Moon. Weather and Earth science are also tested.

Physical Sciences (Science-04)

These questions test what students know about various forces and forms of energy.

WHAT DO MY STUDENTS NEED TO KNOW ABOUT THE ITBS?

The following approaches can help students before the actual ITBS administration.

Ease Students' Minds while Motivating Them

- Let students know that the ITBS is not a test of how smart they are. It is a test that lets them show the skills and facts they have learned in class, and what they have yet to learn.
- Emphasize that the ITBS will not affect students' grades, but that they should do their best because the test is important in a different way. It helps show what they've learned over this year and previous years.

Give Students the Facts about the Test

- Explain the difference between standardized tests and classroom tests. Point out the importance of each kind of test.
- Explain to students that they will probably come across some questions that are difficult for them to answer. They may see questions that require skills or facts they have not learned at all. This test is designed to have some very difficult questions, so they should not get discouraged. All students will have trouble with some questions.
- Check to be sure that your students must take the Complete Battery version of the ITBS. If so, let them know the number of science questions they will see and how much time they will have to answer them (see page 10 for this information). The science questions will all be in one section. There will also be math, reading, writing, and social studies questions in separate sections.
- Find out from the test coordinator at your school how many days your students will have to take all of the ITBS sections. Reassure students that they will have more than one day to take the test.

Familiarize Students with the Testing Situation

- Remind students that standardized tests are not group activities, so they will have to work alone.
- If students are not used to using a separate answer sheet, be sure to explain this process and provide some practice using one in advance of the real test. The answer sheet on page 14 can help you do this.
- The ITBS is a timed test, so students should work carefully and not allow themselves to get stuck on any one question. Working carefully but steadily, most students should be able to answer all or most of the questions.
- Try to determine which students feel anxious about the test and which are overconfident. Some students need to be reassured about their abilities, while others need to be made aware of careless errors they sometimes make.

Provide Basic Test-taking Tips for the ITBS

- ✔ Listen to all of the directions the teacher reads aloud.
- ✔ Read all directions in the test booklet carefully.
- ✔ Read each question and answer choice carefully. Always read all the choices.
- ✔ Examine any graphics that accompany the question.
- ✔ Use your time wisely. Don't get stuck on difficult questions.
- ✔ Use the process of elimination. (See page 6 for one way to introduce the process of elimination to students in class.)
- ✔ Answer each question, even when you have not narrowed down the choices to just one answer. This is especially important for the ITBS.
- ✔ Many science questions on the ITBS have a "second best" answer that is hard to eliminate. Even if you can eliminate only one or two choices, you should pick an answer and mark it.

Provide Tips for Answering the Questions with Short Passages

The ITBS science section often includes short passages describing experiments. We have included these types of passages with multiple-choice questions in the unit tests so that students can practice the skills they will need to do well on the ITBS.

These short passages require basic comprehension skills and strategies. In particular, students must be able to infer cause-and-effect relationships. For all of these types of questions, instruct students to do the following:

1. Read the short passage carefully.
2. Read the first question.
3. Go back to the passage and use the information there, along with your knowledge of what happens in scientific experiments, to figure out the answer.
4. Read the answer choices.
5. Eliminate choices not supported by the passage and your knowledge of science.
6. Choose the answer choice closest to the one you have thought of.

The best way to make sure students understand these steps is to answer one of these questions as a class. Work through each step aloud.

Another important way to be sure students are ready for these types of questions is by reviewing the general purposes and procedures of scientific experiments.

Name: ______________________________ **Date:** ______________

Unit Number: ______________________

1 Ⓐ Ⓑ Ⓒ Ⓓ

2 Ⓕ Ⓖ Ⓗ Ⓙ

3 Ⓐ Ⓑ Ⓒ Ⓓ

4 Ⓕ Ⓖ Ⓗ Ⓙ

5 Ⓐ Ⓑ Ⓒ Ⓓ

6 Ⓕ Ⓖ Ⓗ Ⓙ

7 Ⓐ Ⓑ Ⓒ Ⓓ

8 Ⓕ Ⓖ Ⓗ Ⓙ

9 Ⓐ Ⓑ Ⓒ Ⓓ

10 Ⓕ Ⓖ Ⓗ Ⓙ

11 Ⓐ Ⓑ Ⓒ Ⓓ

12 Ⓕ Ⓖ Ⓗ Ⓙ

13 Ⓐ Ⓑ Ⓒ Ⓓ

14 Ⓕ Ⓖ Ⓗ Ⓙ

15 Ⓐ Ⓑ Ⓒ Ⓓ

16 Ⓕ Ⓖ Ⓗ Ⓙ

17 Ⓐ Ⓑ Ⓒ Ⓓ

18 Ⓕ Ⓖ Ⓗ Ⓙ

19 Ⓐ Ⓑ Ⓒ Ⓓ

20 Ⓕ Ⓖ Ⓗ Ⓙ

21 Ⓐ Ⓑ Ⓒ Ⓓ

22 Ⓕ Ⓖ Ⓗ Ⓙ

23 Ⓐ Ⓑ Ⓒ Ⓓ

24 Ⓕ Ⓖ Ⓗ Ⓙ

25 Ⓐ Ⓑ Ⓒ Ⓓ

Name: ______________________ Date: ______________

Unit One

Directions: Read each question and choose the best answer. Mark your answer on your answer sheet.

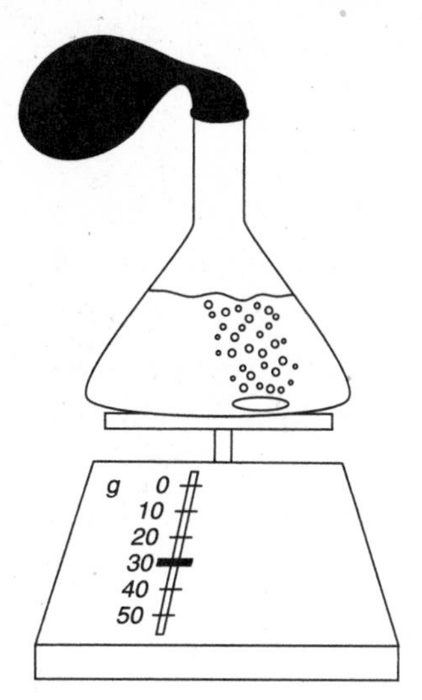

1 What should the scale read when the chemical change in the test tube is finished?

A Where it was at the beginning of the experiment

B Higher than at the beginning of the experiment

C Lower than at the beginning of the experiment

D Equal to zero

2 Why is there a balloon over the top of the glass tube?

J The balloon will catch the gas being made.

K The balloon will catch the water as it bubbles up.

L The balloon will make the water evaporate.

M The balloon will keep the scale at 0 g.

3 Today we use mostly fossil fuels, such as oil and coal, to provide us with energy for electricity. Scientists are working to improve our ability to use other energy sources. **What kind of energy is captured by a dam?**

A Solar energy from the Sun

B Fossil fuels

C Nuclear energy from Earth's core

D Potential energy in stored water

4 When litmus paper is dipped into a mystery substance, it turns blue. Which of these could be the mystery substance?

J Lemon juice

K Battery acid

L Soap

M Vinegar

5 What is the volume of the block that was dropped into the beaker of water?

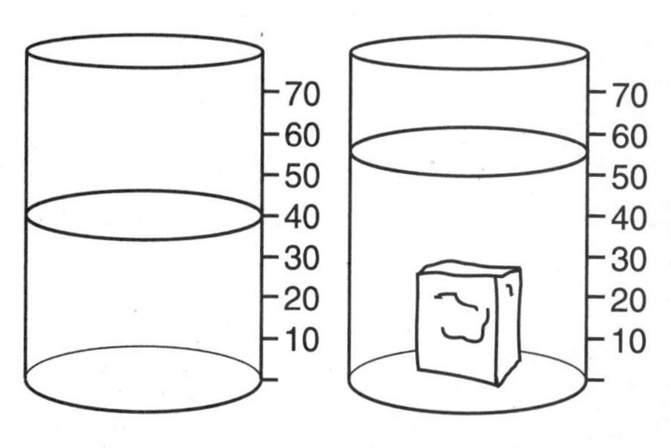

A 40 ml

B 55 ml

C 15 ml

D 25 ml

Name: ______________________ Date: ____________

6 **What can be concluded about corn oil and water from looking at the picture?**

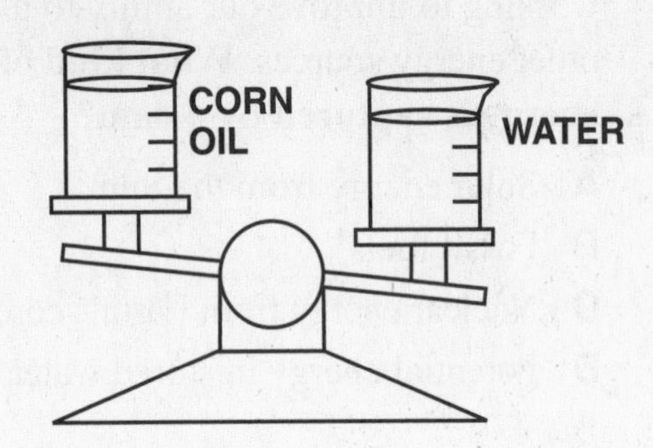

J Corn oil and water have the same density.
K Corn oil is more dense than water.
L Corn oil weighs more than water.
M Water is more dense than corn oil.

7 **What is oxygen at room temperature?**

A Gas
B Liquid
C Solid
D Solution

8 **Which of the following is not a physical change?**

J Water boiling
K Wood burning
L Ice melting
M Cutting cloth

9 **A person floats better in water if he or she takes a deep breath. What is the most likely reason for this?**

A Taking a deep breath pushes water away from you.
B Taking a deep breath makes a person more dense.
C Taking a deep breath makes a person weigh more.
D Taking a deep breath makes a person less dense.

10 **Which of the following is not a metallic element?**

J Chlorine
K Aluminum
L Iron
M Copper

11 **The picture shows what scientists thought was inside an atom one hundred years ago and what they think is inside an atom today. How has their thinking changed?**

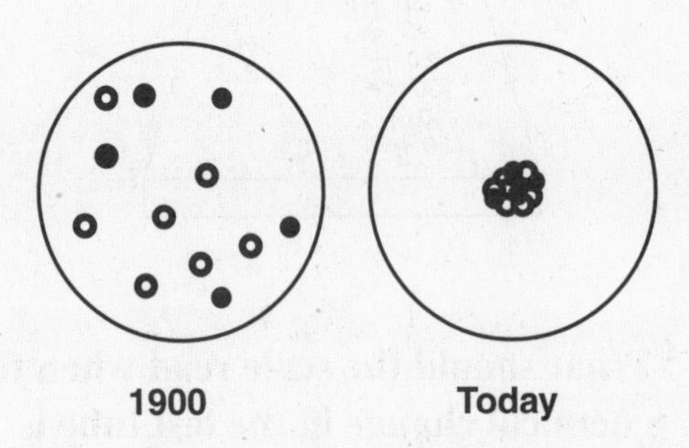

A Scientists used to that think the parts of an atom were all packed in the center, but now they think that they are spread all over the atom.
B Scientists used to think that atoms were empty, but now they think that they are full of smaller parts.
C Scientists used to think that the parts of atoms were lined up inside the atom, but now they think that they are packed in the middle of the atom.
D Scientists used to think the parts of an atom were spread all over the atom, but now they think that they are packed in the center of the atom.

Name: ______________________ Date: ______________

12 **How is a gas different from a solid?**

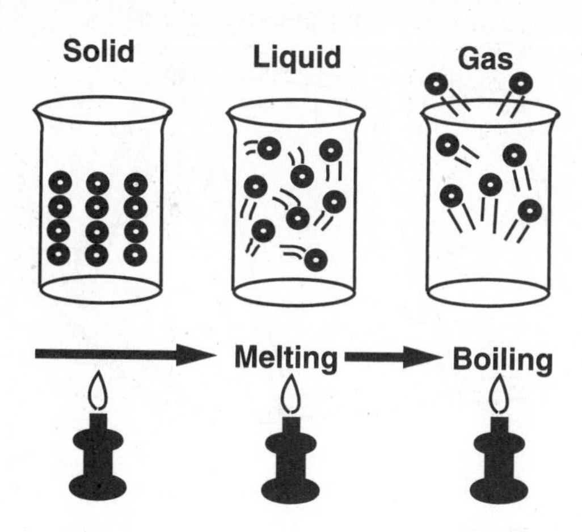

J Gas particles are packed tightly together, but solid particles move quickly.

K Solid particles move faster than gas particles.

L Solid particles are closer together than gas particles.

M Gas particles are colder than solid particles.

13 **What will litmus paper do when it is dipped into a glass containing acid rain?**

A Turn blue

B Turn red

C Turn yellow

D Turn green

14 **What is wrong with the way this experiment is designed?**

J The water container should have more water in it.

K There shouldn't be any heat lamp.

L The heat lamp should be the same distance from the sand and water.

M There should be only one thermometer.

15 **What do scientists look for when creating a material to use as insulation?**

A Something that is expensive

B Something that is not a good conductor of heat

C Something that lets heat escape through it

D Something that melts easily

16 Two balloons were blown up to be the same size. One was held down in a container of hot water. **The other was held down in a container of cold water. What happened?**

J Both balloons probably popped.

K The balloon in cold water got larger than the balloon in hot water.

L The balloons stayed the same size.

M The balloon in hot water got larger than the balloon in cold water.

Name: ______________________ Date: ______________

17 **What happens to the pressure in a car's tires when the season changes from winter to summer?**

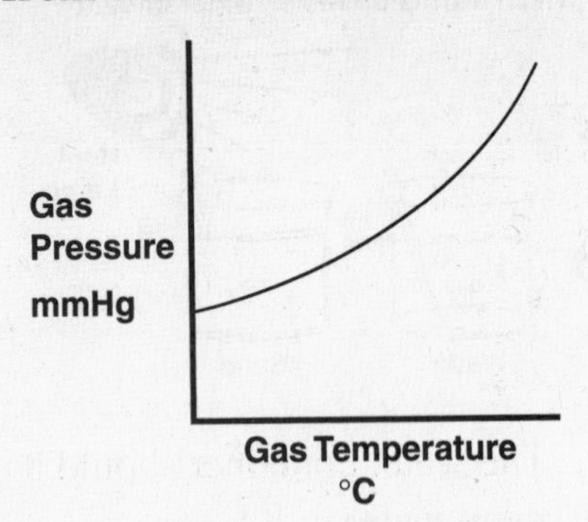

A The pressure of the air in the tires stays the same.

B The pressure of the air in the tires goes up.

C The pressure of the air in the tires goes down.

D The pressure of the air will make the tires deflate.

18 **What is this experiment trying to test?**

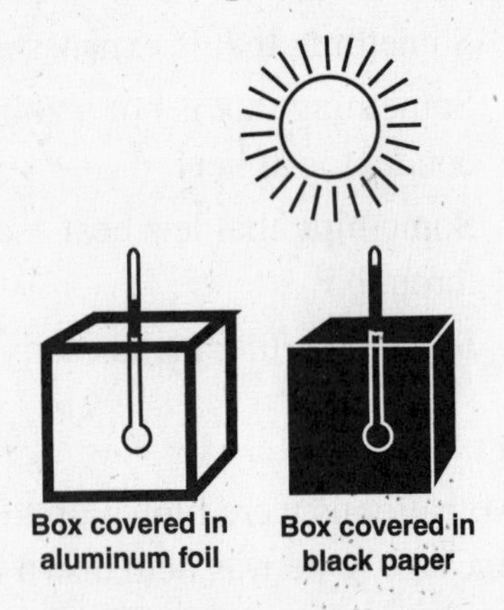

J Whether dark or shiny surfaces absorb the Sun's energy better

K If a box's size affects its temperature

L Whether thermometers work better in black boxes or shiny boxes

M If the shape of a box affects its temperature

19 **What is the purpose of the solar panels on this person's roof?**

A To keep water from hitting the roof

B To send and receive radio waves

C To collect sunlight and use it to heat the house

D To reflect sunlight back into space

Name: ______________________ Date: ____________

Unit Two

Directions: Read each question and choose the best answer. Mark your answer on your answer sheet.

1 Which of these is not found in any human cells?

A Nucleus
B Mitochondrion
C Chloroplast
D Cell membrane

2 A scientist performs research on how cell growth is controlled. Which of the following is caused by body cells growing out of control?

J AIDS
K Blindness
L Heart attacks
M Cancer

3 Which organisms are most likely responsible for breaking down and eating dead leaves, trees, and animals in a forest?

A Squirrels
B Herbivores
C Owls
D Slugs

4 Biologists have organized all living species into categories. Which statement explains what all the animals in the picture have in common?

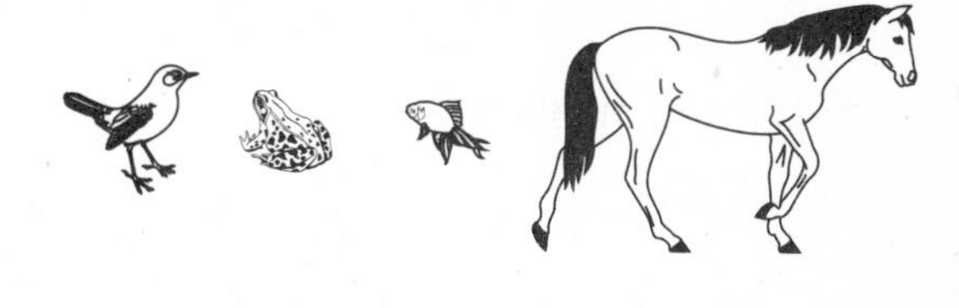

J All of these animals are amphibians.
K All of these animals are herbivores.
L All of these animals have bones.
M All of these animals lay eggs.

5 Andre's science class is learning about microorganisms found in pond water. Which piece of equipment should Andre use to look at microorganisms?

A Telescope
B Flashlight
C Microscope
D Binoculars

6 Which is not a characteristic that all living things share?

J Ability to grow
K Ability to make food from sunlight
L Ability to reproduce
M Ability to respond to the surroundings

Name: ______________________ Date: ______________

7 **What does Wendy need to add to her fish tank to make it a complete ecosystem that can survive without her help?**

A Birds
B Fish
C Water plants
D People

8 **How much of your body is made up of oxygen and carbon?**

ELEMENTS THAT MAKE UP THE HUMAN BODY		
Symbol	Element	Percent
O	Oxygen	65.0
C	Carbon	18.5
H	Hydrogen	9.5
N	Nitrogen	3.3
Ca	Calcium	1.5
P	Phosphorous	1.0
K	Potassium	0.4
S	Sulfur	0.3
Na	Sodium	0.2
Cl	Chlorine	0.2
Mg	Magnesium	0.1

J 65%
K 18.5%
L 28%
M 83.5%

9 **What percent of a human cell is not water?**

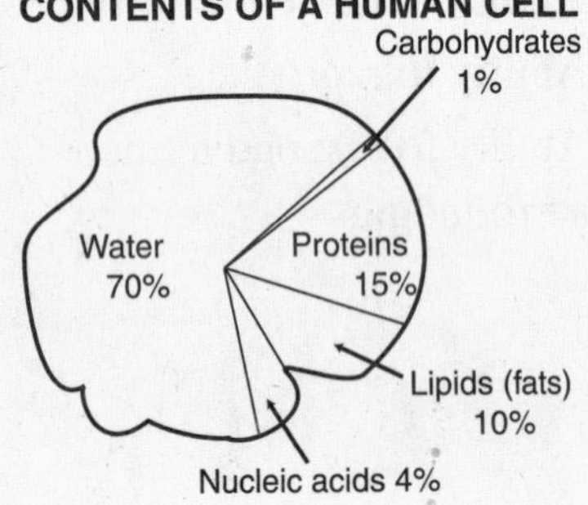

A 70%
B 30%
C 15%
D 25%

10 **Which invention allowed scientists to prove that all living things contain cells?**

J The microscope
K The telescope
L The x-ray machine
M The computer

11 **What does the picture tell you about the cell membrane?**

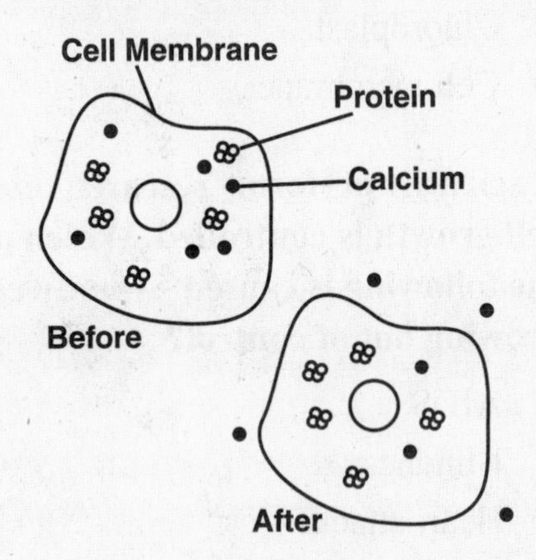

A It lets anything move across it.
B Calcium can diffuse across it, but protein cannot.
C It lets only large molecules diffuse across it.
D Protein can diffuse across it, but calcium cannot.

Name: ______________________ Date: ______________

12 **How do plants and animals use oxygen?**

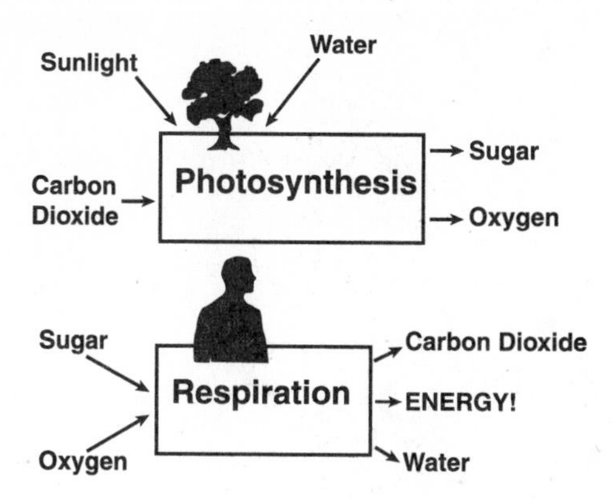

J Plants use oxygen during photosynthesis and animals make oxygen during respiration.

K Plants make oxygen during respiration and animals use oxygen during photosynthesis.

L Plants make oxygen during photosynthesis and animals use oxygen during respiration.

M Plants use oxygen during respiration and animals make oxygen during photosynthesis.

13 **Which of the following is a fungus?**

A Pine tree

B Amoeba

C Clam

D Mushroom

14 **What do all members of the plant kingdom have in common?**

J All plants are herbivores.

K All plants make their own food.

L All plants move from one place to another.

M All plants are vertebrates.

15 **What word should go in the empty space in the table?**

ANIMALS WITH BACKBONES	
Animal Class	Outer Covering
Birds	Feathers
Reptiles	Dry Scales
Fish	Wet Scales
Mammals	

A Fins

B Shells

C Body hair

D Milk

16 **Why do tomato plants produce seeds inside the tomato?**

J To make the tomato taste better

K To reproduce and make more tomato plants

L To help the plant make food from the Sun

M To make the tomatoes grow faster

Name: ______________________ Date: ______________

17 A science class performs an experiment to test what keeps bacteria from growing in apple juice. They did different things to containers of apple juice and then checked them three days later.

	Apple Juice	Apple Juice	Apple Juice	Apple Juice
What was done:	Boiled then covered	Frozen	Salt added then covered	Left on window in science room
What happened:	Juice is still clear	Juice is still clear	Juice is still clear	Juice is cloudy with bacteria

What can be concluded from the results?

A Boiling keeps bacteria from growing but freezing doesn't.

B Salt is the only way to keep bacteria from growing in apple juice.

C Bacteria can't grow in apple juice.

D Bacteria will grow in apple juice if it is left alone.

18 **Why did the class need to have a container of apple juice with nothing special done to it?**

J To be able to make comparisons with the other containers

K Because they did not have any grape juice

L Because all experiments need four parts to them

M To compare how different brands of apple juice grow bacteria

19 **Which of the pictures does not belong in the same family as the others?**

A

B

C

D

20 **What is the process by which all living organisms produce offspring called?**

J Reproduction

K Classification

L Respiration

M Excretion

Name: ______________________ Date: ____________

Unit Three

Directions: Read each question and choose the best answer. Mark your answer on your answer sheet.

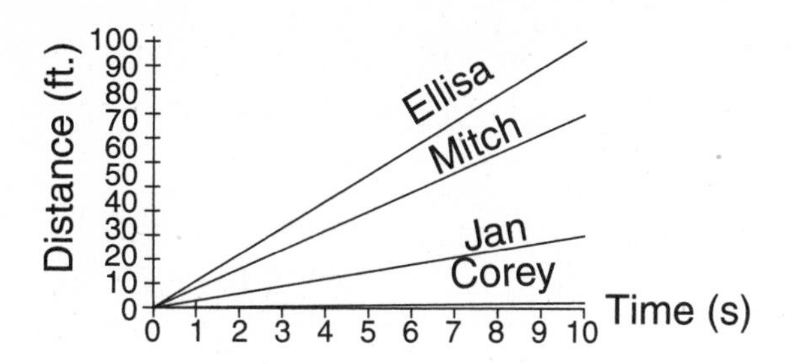

1 Jan, Mitch, Ellisa, and Corey are racing each other. The graph shows how far they each got after 10 seconds. **Which runner was traveling at the highest speed?**

A Jan
B Mitch
C Ellisa
D Corey

2 **Which runner ran at a constant speed?**

J Jan
K Mitch
L Ellisa
M Corey

3 Energy can exist in many forms and can be changed from one form to another. Most cars move by burning gasoline to release chemical energy. Some cars use energy from solar power. **What kind of energy change occurs to make a solar-powered car run?**

A Mechanical energy is being changed into light energy
B Heat energy is being changed into sound energy
C Light energy is being changed into mechanical energy
D Electrical is being changed energy into potential energy

4 **Which surface would exert the least frictional force on your feet as you walk?**

J Ice
K Rug
L Sidewalk
M Grass

Name: ______________________ Date: ______________

5 **Many car accidents occur because cars are traveling too quickly to make it safely around a turn. Which technological improvements in cars help to keep people safe in their seats around curves?**

A Headlights
B Mufflers
C Windshields
D Seat belts

6 **Jan parks in the parking lot of the city park and walks to the playground. Which direction is she walking?**

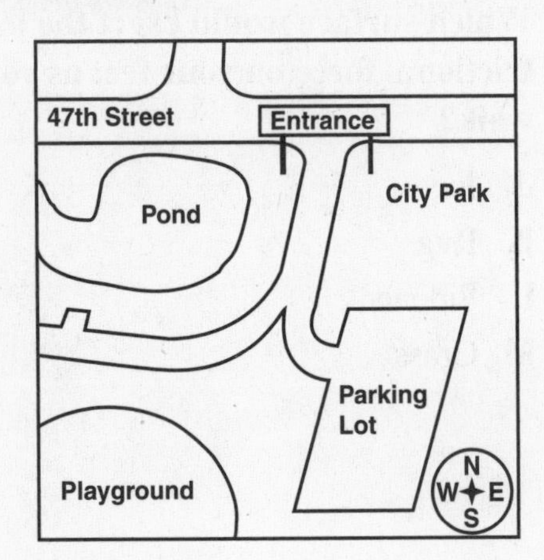

J North
K South
L East
M West

7 **When a car's speed increases, it is called**

A Acceleration
B Position
C Gravity
D Friction

Directions: Use the information below to answer questions 8 and 9.

Slope of ramp (in degrees)	Distance ball rolls (in cm)
45	105
35	84
25	62

8 **What can be concluded about balls rolling down ramps from this experiment?**

J The steeper the slope, the shorter the distance the ball rolls.
K The heavier the ball, the shorter the distance the ball rolls.
L The steeper the slope, the further the distance the ball rolls.
M The steepness of the slope doesn't affect how far the ball rolls.

9 **What would be the most likely distance the ball would roll after going down a ramp with a 15-degree slope?**

A 0 cm
B 45 cm
C 95 cm
D 125 cm

Name: ______________________________ Date: ______________

10 **A bike slows down when its brakes rub against its wheel. What kind of force is being applied to the wheel by the brakes?**

J Acceleration
K Centripetal
L Friction
M Potential

11 **When a ball is thrown up into the air, what makes it come back down again?**

A Air pressure
B Wind
C Speed
D Gravity

12 Scientists have tried to design airplanes so that they move through the air as easily as possible. They design boats so that they move through water as easily as possible. **What kind of force causes airplanes and boats to slow down as they move forward?**

J Drag force
K Weight
L Balanced force
M Newton

13 **The heavier a moving object is, the more momentum it has. Which object has the most momentum?**

A A bike going 5 miles per hour
B A school bus going 5 miles per hour
C A person running 5 miles per hour
D A small car going 5 miles per hour

14 **Which object has the most kinetic energy?**

J A bowling ball rolling 5 ft/s
K A golf ball rolling 5 ft/s
L A bowling ball rolling 20 ft/s
M A golf ball rolling 20 ft/s

15 **How do batteries make a radio work?**

A The battery has stored energy in it that can be changed into electricity.
B The battery has stored sounds in it that come out of the radio speakers.
C The battery takes energy from the radio to make it work.
D The chemicals move from the battery into the radio to make sound.

Name: ______________________ Date: ______________

16 **When Mary lets go of her pendulum, what will happen when the pendulum swings back toward her?**

J The pendulum will swing higher.
K The pendulum will not swing as high.
L The pendulum will swing back to the same height.
M The pendulum will stop swinging.

17 **Many countries use coal, natural gas, and oil as sources of energy for motor vehicles and electricity. What does it mean to conserve these natural sources of energy?**

A To sell as much of them as possible
B To use as little as necessary because they might run out
C To trade them with other countries around the world
D To try to discover more of these energy sources in the ground

18 **What do all of these simple machines have in common?**

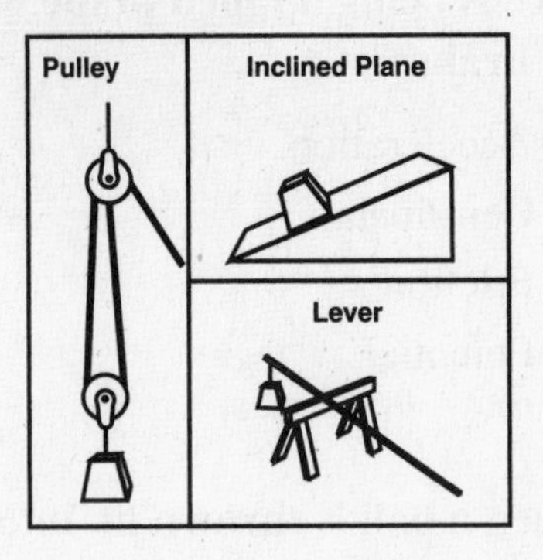

J They all make it easier to do work.
K They all make it harder to do work.
L They all work without any friction.
M They all have many parts.

19 **When Sean pulls down on the pulley rope, what will happen?**

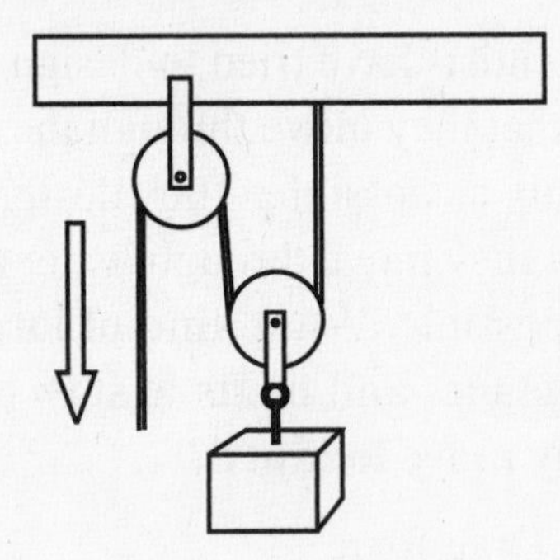

A The block will go down, too.
B The block will go up.
C The block will not move.
D The block will move to the left.

Name: ______________________ Date: ____________

Unit Four

Directions: Read each question and choose the best answer. Mark your answer on your answer sheet.

1 **Bridget's science class is walking through Central Park in New York. They are investigating where the Sun is in the sky at different times of day. It is 5:00 PM and the Sun is warming Bridget's back as she walks. Which direction is she walking?**

A North
B South
C East
D West

2 **Jay looks up at the sky one night. There are no clouds in the sky. Then a round shadow slowly moves across the Moon. After a while, the Moon is covered completely by the shadow. Hours later, the shadow has moved off the Moon and Jay can see the Moon again. What has he just seen?**

J A lunar eclipse
K A solar eclipse
L A sunset
M A meteorite

3 **Which statement best explains the changes Jay watched?**

A The Moon was hidden behind some clouds.
B An airplane flew in front of the Moon.
C Earth moved between the Sun and the Moon.
D The Moon stopped giving off light for a little while.

4 **When it is summer in North America, what season is it in South America?**

J Summer
K Winter
L Spring
M Fall

5 **Which of these gives off its own light?**

A Saturn
B Star
C Moon
D Jupiter

Name: ______________________ Date: __________

6 **Instead of moving in straight lines, the planets orbit the Sun. What causes this?**

J Gravity of the Sun
K Inertia
L The other planets
M The Moon

7 **Which instrument would be most useful for learning more about the planet Mars?**

A Microscope
B Telescope
C Magnifying glass
D X-ray machine

8 **When NASA wants to send astronauts into space to do experiments and then bring them back when the experiments are done, they use a**

J space shuttle.
K star.
L satellite.
M missle.

9 **Water used by the astronauts is purified and reused. Why do they need to recycle water in a spacecraft?**

A Because they can collect water from outer space
B Because they need water to power the spacecraft
C Because they can only bring small amounts of water with them
D Because they need to breathe water vapor

Directions: Use the table below to answer questions 10 and 11.

PAST SPACE MISSIONS

Year	Spacecraft	Carrying Crew?	Mission
1958	Explorer III	No	Discovered Earth's radiation belt
1966	Surveyor I	No	First American soft landing on Moon's surface
1969	Apollo 11	Yes	First landing by humans on the Moon
1972	Pioneer 10	No	Flew by and took pictures of Jupiter
1990	Hubble Space Telescope	No	Took pictures of stars and collision of comet with Jupiter
1996	Mars Pathfinder	No	Sent remote-controlled car to take pictures of surface of Mars

10 **When did humans first land on the Moon?**

J 1958
K 1966
L 1969
M 1996

11 **Why was the Hubble Space Telescope sent into space?**

A To land on the Moon
B To land on Mars and take pictures
C To fly by Jupiter
D To take pictures of stars and planets

12 **If you are walking and your shadow is stretched out in front of you, where is the Sun?**

J In front of you
K Behind you
L On your left side
M Directly overhead

Name: ______________________ Date: ______________

13 **Which picture shows the correct shadow pattern for the pencil at sunrise?**

A

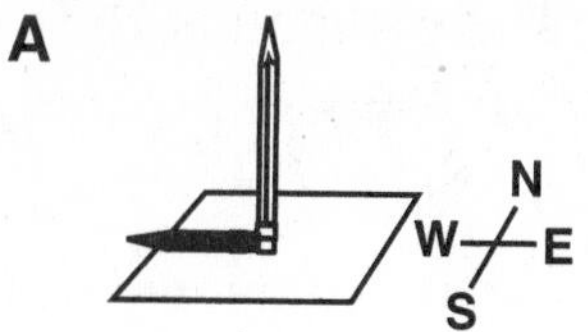

B

C

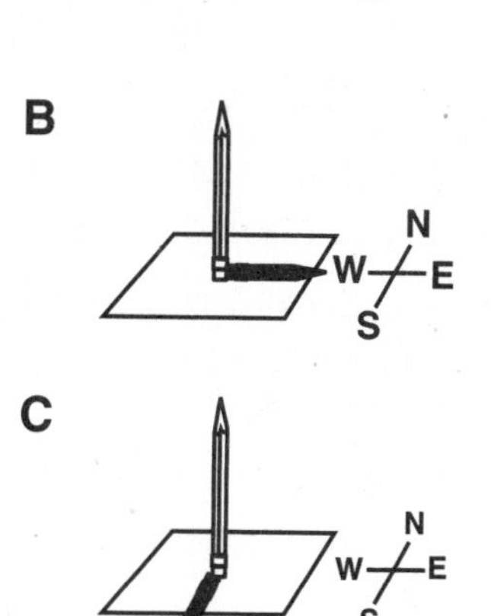

D

14 **If it is 6:00 p.m. in Miami, FL, what time is it in San Francisco, CA?**

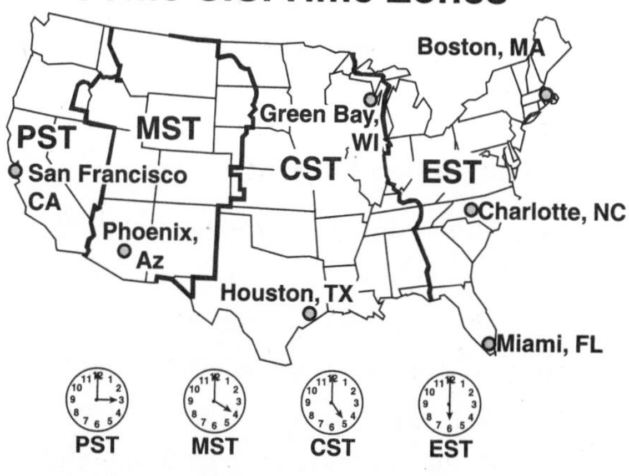

J 9:00 PM

K 3:00 AM

L 3:00 PM

M 4:00 AM

15 **Which of the following cities sees the sunrise first each day?**

A San Francisco, CA

B Phoenix, AZ

C Green Bay, WI

D Boston, MA

16 **Which part of the water cycle uses the Sun as a source of energy to make it happen?**

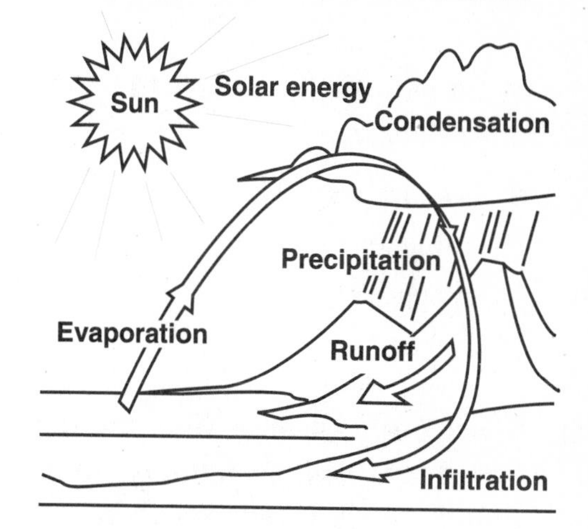

J Runoff

K Infiltration

L Evaporation

M Precipitation

17 **The gravity of the Moon and the Sun pull on Earth's oceans, making them rise and fall along the shore. This is called**

A The tides

B An eclipse

C Precipitation

D The seasons

Name: ______________________________ Date: ______________

18 Marty looked up at the night sky on January 10 and January 20. He noticed that one light had moved.

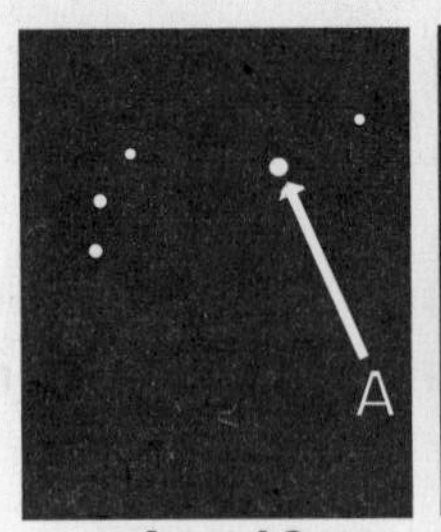

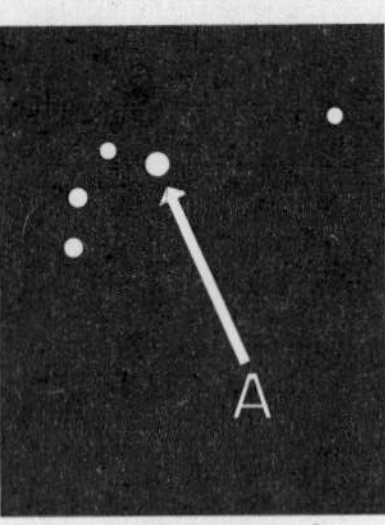

Jan 10 Jan 20

What was the light marked "A" most likely?

J An airplane
K A planet
L A space station
M A star

19 **Space probes sent to Mercury and Venus have sent back information that there are lava flows on both of these planets. What probably caused these lava flows?**

A Earthquakes
B Erosion from water
C Volcanoes on the planets' surfaces
D Space probes from Earth

20 **Earth's atmosphere has lots of oxygen in it, but there is no oxygen in the atmospheres on Mercury, Venus, or Mars. Where did all of the oxygen in Earth's atmosphere probably come from?**

J Stars exploding from intense heat
K Plants on Earth giving off oxygen during photosynthesis
L Animals breathing out oxygen and breathing in carbon dioxide
M Air coming down from outer space through the atmosphere

21 The alcohol in a thermometer expands and contracts when the temperature changes.

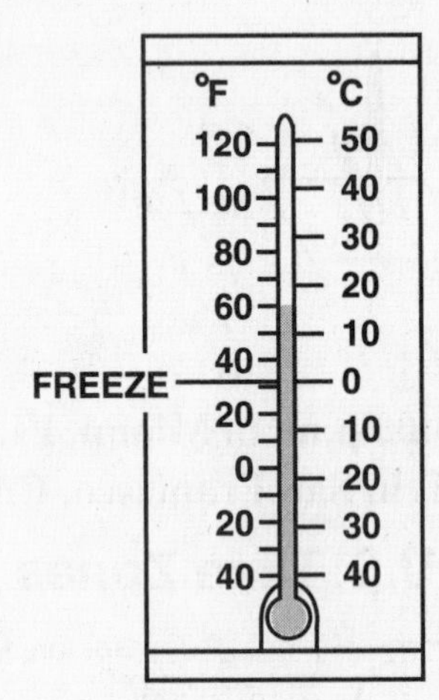

What makes the alcohol rise?

A When it gets colder, the alcohol expands and moves up the tube.
B When it gets warmer, the alcohol contracts and moves down the tube.
C When it gets colder, more alcohol comes into the tube from the air.
D When it gets warmer, the alcohol expands and moves up the tube.

Name: ______________________ Date: ______________

Unit Five

Directions: Read each question and choose the best answer. Mark your answer on your answer sheet.

1 Geologists believe that Earth's continents were bunched together millions of years ago. Slowly, Earth's crust has moved, spreading the continents apart to the positions they are in today. **According to this theory, which is the oldest picture of Earth?**

A

B

C

D

2 **What is another name for huge moving fields of ice?**

J Magma
K Glaciers
L Bedrock
M Mantle

3 A geologist discovers an unusual-looking fossil buried in a canyon wall made of sedimentary rock. Further along the wall, she finds a second fossil in a different layer of the sedimentary rock. **How can she make a guess about which fossil is older?**

A Smaller fossils are always older.
B The oldest layers of rock are always granite.
C Older fossils are always more cracked.
D The fossil in a deeper layer of sedimentary rock is usually older.

4 **How was the Grand Canyon created?**

J Earthquakes
K Volcanoes
L A fault
M Erosion by rivers

5 **Soil is formed over thousands of years. What starts the process of making soil?**

A Weathering of rock
B Animals
C Lava from volcanoes
D Humus

Name: ______________________ Date: ____________

6 **Which of the following is an example of Earth's crust moving?**

J Fossils
K Hurricanes
L Earthquakes
M Waves

7 **Which area of this ocean floor was made most recently?**

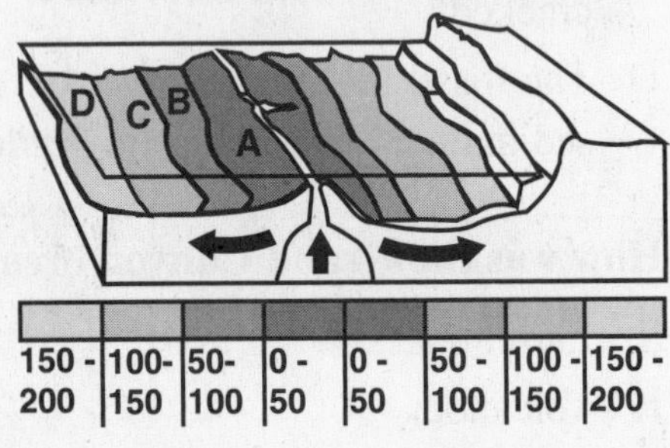

A Area A
B Area B
C Area C
D Area D

8 **Which of the following is a natural resource that comes from Earth's crust?**

J Wood
K Coal
L Cloth
M Rain

9 **The west coast of Africa and the east coast of South America have matching shapes, almost like two fitting puzzle pieces. What does this suggest?**

A There used to be no Atlantic Ocean.
B They were eroded in the same way by the ocean.
C They were next to each other millions of years ago.
D There are the same animals living in Africa and South America.

10 **Why are fossils usually shells, bones, or teeth?**

J Because all of these parts are hard and last long enough to be preserved
K Because all of these parts are soft and decay quickly
L Because all of these parts are found in every living thing
M Because all of these parts were found in ancient animals, but not in animals living today

Name: ______________________ Date: __________

11 **When sedimentary rocks in the crust are exposed to heat and pressure, what kind of rock can they change into?**

A Igneous rock
B Sedimentary rock
C Metamorphic rock
D Humus

12 **Which is not a way that scientists divide minerals into categories?**

J By hardness
K By texture
L By structure
M By taste

Use the information below to answer questions 13–15.

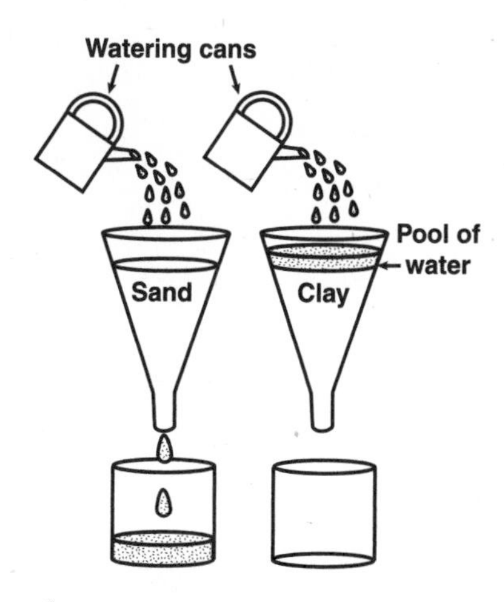

13 **What is this experiment most likely trying to test?**

A Whether water flows better through sand or clay
B Which is the best kind of watering can
C Which kind of soil seeds grow best in
D How much sand can fit in a funnel

14 **If gravel was also going to be tested in the experiment above, which funnel should be added to compare to the others?**

J
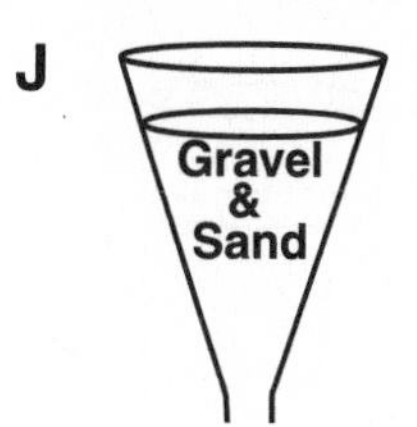

K
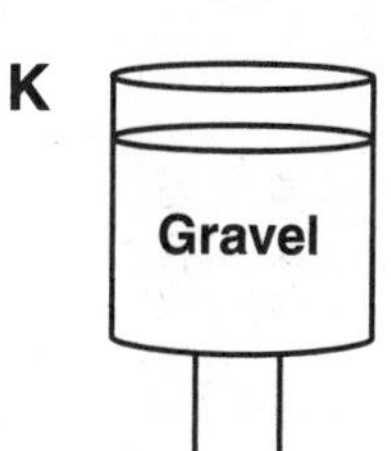

L
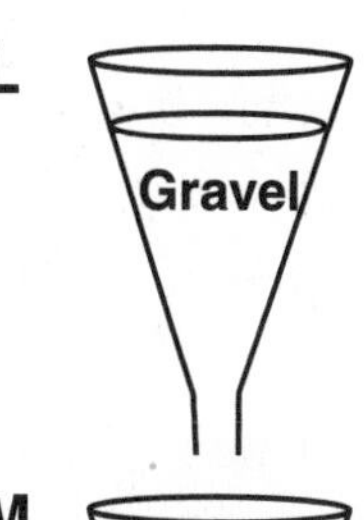

M
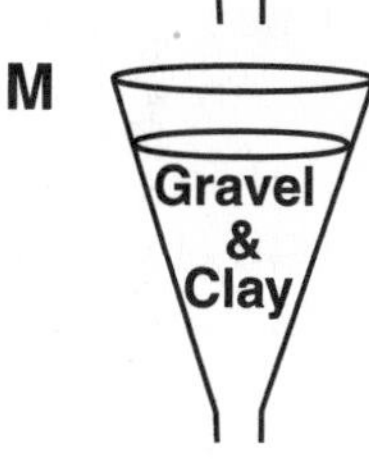

15 **How could farmers use the results of this experiment to make their crops grow better?**

A They could use the results to choose a soil that helps rain get to plant roots better.
B They could put lots of clay in their fields to let rain seep into the roots of their crops.
C They could grow their crops in mud.
D They could add fertilizers to their soil.

Name: ____________________ Date: ____________

16 **What can be concluded from this experiment about water when it freezes?**

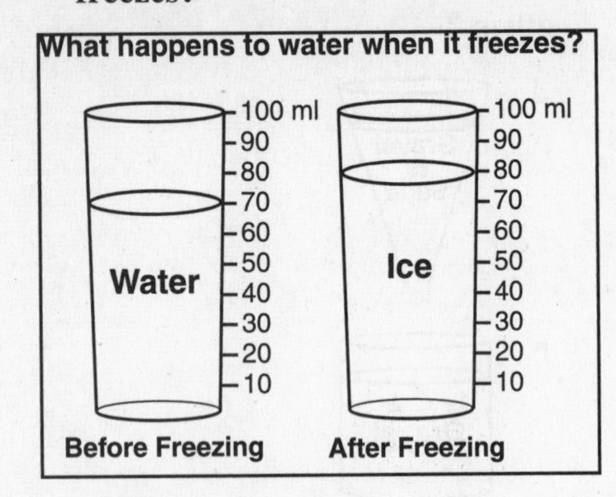

J Water changes into another liquid when it freezes.

K Water expands when it turns into ice.

L Water has a volume of 80 ml every time it freezes.

M Water contracts when it turns into ice.

17 **When water seeps into cracks in rocks and then freezes, what might happen?**

A The water may turn the rock into metamorphic rock.

B The ice may act as glue to seal the cracks permanently.

C The rocks may be broken apart when the water expands.

D The water will contract and pull the rock together at the cracks.

18 **What does it mean when a volcano is dormant?**

J It is currently erupting.

K It has been inactive for a long time, but did erupt in the past.

L It has never erupted and probably will never erupt.

M It is a very small volcano.

19 **In what areas of the world do architects build bridges and buildings with flexible materials?**

A Areas where volcanic eruptions are likely

B Areas that are very cold

C Areas where earthquakes are likely

D Areas where few people live

Name: ______________________ Date: __________

Unit Six

Directions: Read each question and choose the best answer. Mark your answer on your answer sheet.

IF YOU ARE BLOOD TYPE	YOU CAN RECEIVE TYPE	YOU CAN DONATE TO PEOPLE WITH TYPE
A	O, A	A, AB
B	O, B	B, AB
AB	AB	O, A, B, AB
O	O	A, B, AB, O

1 **Georgette is in the hospital and needs someone to donate blood to her. Her blood type is B. Which kind(s) of blood can she receive?**

A A or O
B B or O
C only B
D B or AB

2 **Several months later, Georgette donates blood at the hospital so that there is blood available when needed. Who could Georgette's blood be given to?**

J People with Type A or O
K People with Type B or O
L People with only Type B
M People with Type B or AB

3 **Heredity is when characteristics are passed on from parents to offspring. Which of these is a trait children inherit from their parents?**

A Where they live
B Eye color
C Age
D Hair length

4 **Regan and her science partner toss a penny 100 times and record how many times it lands heads-up or tails-up. What was the most likely number of times her penny landed heads-up?**

J 100
K 1
L 56
M 0

5 In 1997, scientists announced that they had created a sheep named Dolly who was a clone. The scientists had taken DNA from an adult sheep and used it to make Dolly. Because Dolly and the other sheep had the same DNA, they were identical. **Which statement best explains why scientists are excited about cloning?**

A There is a shortage of sheep around the world.
B Scientists might be able to clone human cells to replace damaged ones in patients.
C Scientists didn't know DNA carried inherited traits.
D Scientists want to use cloning to make many new kinds of sheep.

6 Jamie's science class is growing pea plants. They move small cotton balls from one flower to the next, imitating the way bees move among flowers. **Why are Jamie and his friends doing this?**

J They are eating the peas.
K They are carrying pollen that fertilizes the flowers.
L They are drying off the flowers.
M They are helping the plants to photosynthesize.

Name: ______________________________ Date: ______________

7 **When pollen from purple pea plant flowers is used to fertilize white pea plant flowers, all of the offspring plants have purple flowers. What kind of trait is purple flower color in peas?**

A A dominant trait

B A recessive trait

C Not an inherited trait

D An incompletely dominant trait

8 **When purple and white pea plants are crossed, all of the offspring plants have purple flowers. What kinds of plants should Melinda's science class get when they cross a tall plant with a short plant?**

	Seed Color	Flower Color	Plant Height
Dominant form	Yellow	Purple	Tall
Recessive form	Green	White	Short

J Half the offspring plants will be short and half will be tall.

K All of the offspring plants will be short.

L All of the offspring plants will be tall.

M Half of the offspring plants will be medium and half will be short or tall.

9 **Peter fills a bag with 50 red jellybeans and 50 black jellybeans. If he reaches into the bag to pull out a jellybean, what is the chance that he'll pull out a black one?**

A 50%

B 1 out of 3

C 100%

D 1 out of 10

10 **Peter pulls out a jelly bean, records what color it is, and then puts it back into the bag. He repeats this 20 times. How many times did he most likely get a red jelly bean?**

J 20

K 1

L 0

M 9

Directions: Use the information below to answer questions 11 and 12

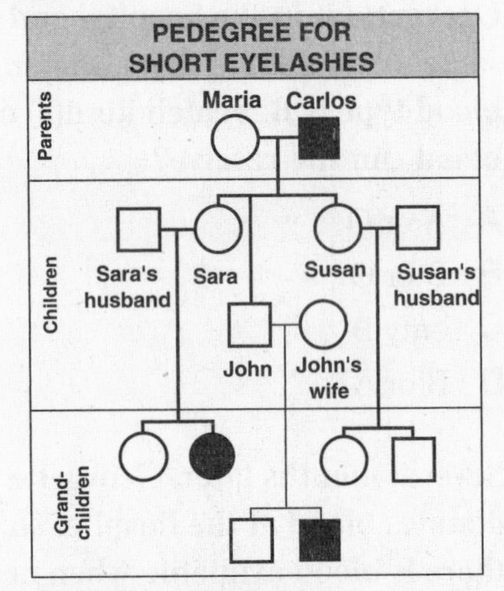

■ Shaded: short eyelashes (recessive trait)

□ Unshaded: long eyelashes (dominant trait)

11 **How many grandsons with long eyelashes do Maria and Carlos have?**

A 1

B 2

C 0

D 3

12 **Sara and her husband have**

J one daughter with long eyelashes and one daughter with short eyelashes.

K one son with long eyelashes and one son with short eyelashes.

L one daughter with long eyelashes and one son with long eyelashes.

M one son with long eyelashes and one daughter with long eyelashes.

Name: ______________________ Date: __________

13 **How does a fertilized egg get all of its chromosomes?**

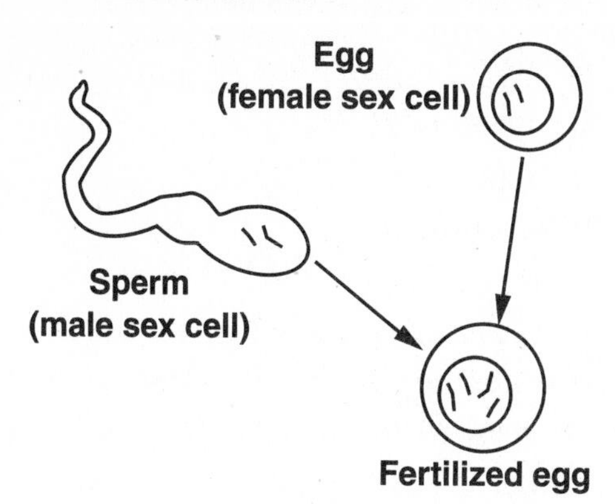

A All from the egg
B All from the sperm
C Half from the egg and half from the sperm
D One quarter from the sperm and three quarters from the egg

14 **What can be concluded from the chart about where a person's inherited traits come from?**

J A person's traits are mostly from the father.
K A person's traits are mostly from the mother.
L A person doesn't inherit any traits.
M A person's traits are a mixture from the mother and father.

15 Many of a person's traits are inherited in her genes. A person's environment can also affect how she functions. **Which of these is an example of an environmental effect?**

A Judy has blue eyes like her mother and father.
B Mark was paralyzed in a car accident.
C Juan is as tall as his father.
D Mike has two dimples like his grandmother and sister.

16 **Scientists believe the woolly mammoth lived in North America more than a million years ago. What evidence do you think they have to support this theory?**

J Books written back then
K Science fiction movies about woolly mammoths
L Fossils of woolly mammoth bones and tusks
M Photographs scientists found

Name: ______________________________ Date: ______________

17 Scientists at the American Museum of Natural History noticed that the labels have fallen off a display showing layers of fossils underground. **Which of the labels should go on the bottom layer of fossils in the picture?**

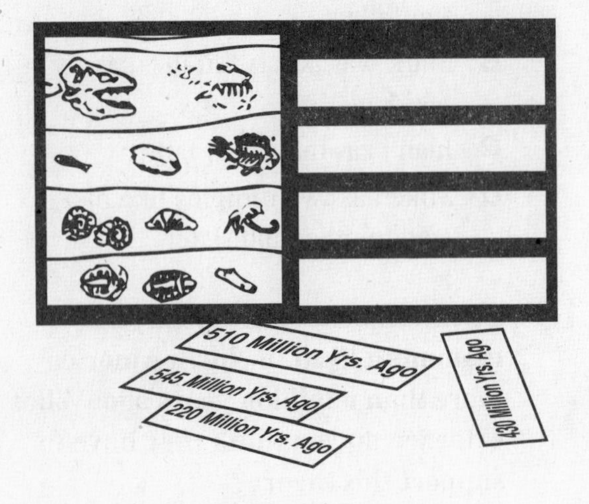

A 430 million years ago
B 545 million years ago
C 510 million years ago
D 220 million years ago

18 **The bones in a bird's wing and a human's arm are similar in number and arrangement. This is evidence that**

Bird Wing

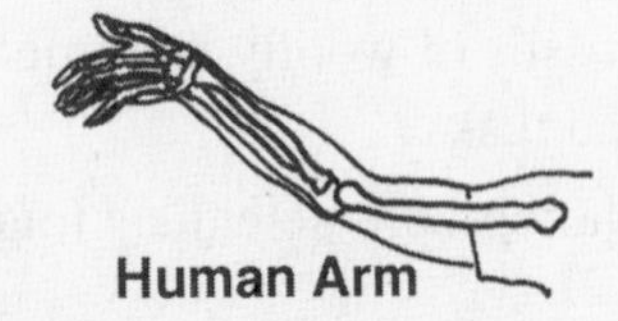
Human Arm

J humans and birds are the same species.
K humans can fly.
L birds are more intelligent than humans.
M humans and birds evolved from a common ancestor.

19 **Dinosaurs had dry, scaly skin so they were probably most like today's**

A fish.
B mammals.
C reptiles.
D amphibians.

20 **How are all of these finches able to survive together in the same cluster of trees, without competing with each other?**

	**MEDIUM GROUND FINCH** Lives on ground Eats large seeds and nuts
	**LARGE GROUND FINCH** Lives on ground Eats buds and fruit
	**LARGE CACTUS GROUND FINCH** Lives on ground Eats small cactus seeds
	**WARBLER FINCH** Lives in trees Eats small insects

J They all eat different things.
K They all eat the same things.
L They all eat insects.
M They all live in trees.

Name: ______________________ Date: ____________

Unit Seven

Directions: Read each question and choose the best answer. Mark your answer on your answer sheet.

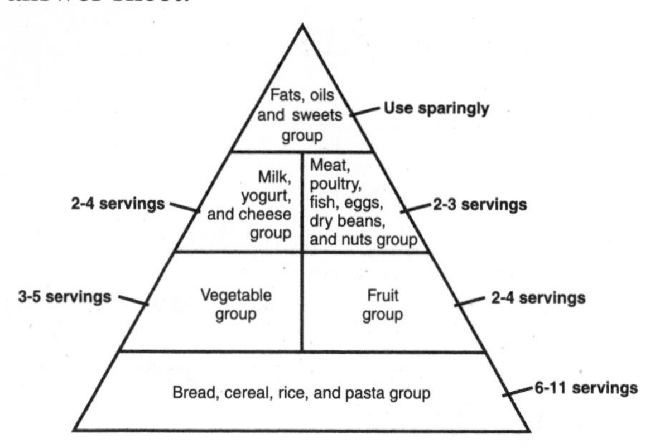

1 **According to the Food Guide Pyramid, which of these foods should you eat most often?**

A Peanuts
B Ham
C Bread
D Cheese

2 **What should you have the least of?**

J Fish
K Candy
L Crackers
M Yogurt

3 **Which of these is a reflex action?**

A Reading
B Blinking
C Jump-roping
D Talking

4 **Which of these is not one of your senses?**

J Smell
K Sight
L Thought
M Hearing

Directions: Use the information below to answer questions 5 and 6.

Helen and three classmates perform an experiment to see the effect of exercise on pulse rate. They took their pulses while sitting down and then after doing jumping jacks.

Name	Pulse Before Exercise	Pulse After Exercise
Helen	60	88
John	55	90
Brianna	70	99
Peter	50	80

5 **What could the students do to make sure the experiment was done fairly?**

A All students should do the jumping jacks at different times of day.
B All students should do the same number of jumping jacks.
C Each student should do a different number of jumping jacks.
D The girls should do more jumping jacks than the boys.

6 **Which organ in the human body is responsible for holding and feeding a growing embryo?**

J Stomach
K Breast
L Ovary
M Uterus

Name: ______________________________ Date: ______________

7 **Which organ in the body is responsible for interpreting and sending messages to your body?**

A Heart
B Stomach
C Brain
D Skin

8 **Reflexes are actions like breathing, coughing, and keeping your balance. How are these actions similar to each other?**

J They are all things your lungs do.
K They are all things your body does automatically.
L They are all related to eating.
M They are all things children cannot do.

9 Nekesa and her partner are studying the sense of taste. This picture shows where your different taste buds are located on your tongue.

THE TONGUE

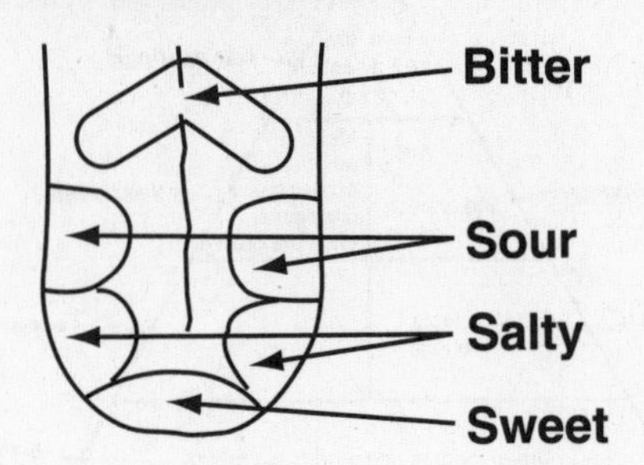

What would you predict would happen when Nekesa drops a piece of sugar at the very tip of her partner's tongue?

A Her partner would taste something bitter.
B Her partner would taste something salty.
C Her partner would taste something sweet.
D Her partner would taste something sour.

Name: ______________________ Date: ____________

10 Jennifer's science partner drops a ruler for her to catch. The first time, she misses it. **What do you predict will happen to her reaction time when she repeats the experiment twenty times?**

J Her reaction time will get faster with practice.

K Her reaction time will stay the same.

L Her reaction time will get slower with practice.

M Her brain will stop sending the message to her fingers to catch the ruler.

11 **What might be the result when a person breaks his spinal cord in an accident?**

A He might be unable to hear very well.

B He might be unable to move his legs anymore.

C He might be unable to see very well.

D He might be unable to remember things.

12 **Doctors can use an electroencephalograph (EEG) to measure brain activity. Which of the following questions might be answered by using an EEG?**

J Does pulse change with exercise?

K What is the function of the human liver?

L What parts of the brain are working while a person sleeps?

M Do cholesterol and high blood pressure cause heart attacks?

13 **When a woman gets older, her ovaries stop releasing eggs each month. This time in her life is called**

A menstruation.

B menopause.

C puberty.

D childbirth.

14 **The pictures show what happens once an egg is fertilized by a sperm. What phrase best describes what change is happening?**

WHAT HAPPENS AFTER AN EGG IS FERTILIZED

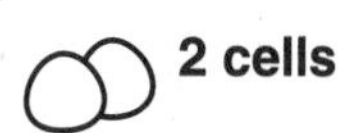

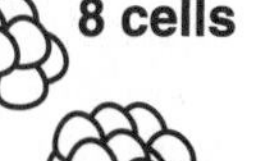

J The egg is making more sperm.

K The arms and legs of the embryo are being created.

L The fertilized egg is dividing many times to make more cells.

M The fertilized egg is becoming twins.

15 **A developing baby inside the mother's uterus is surrounded by**

A air.

B fluid-filled sac.

C a hard shell.

D the mother's ribcage.

Name: ______________________ Date: ______________

16 **Twins who are identical developed from one original egg and sperm. Twins who are not identical**

- **J** developed from one original egg and sperm as well.
- **K** are born in different years.
- **L** are always female.
- **M** developed from two different eggs and sperm.

17 **What are the walls of the mother's uterus made of in order to help her push out the baby during childbirth?**

- **A** Muscle
- **B** Bone
- **C** Skin
- **D** Food

18 **Which of the following is a sexually transmitted disease?**

- **J** Chicken pox
- **K** AIDS
- **L** Influenza
- **M** Cancer

19 **For homework you are asked to learn the alphabet backwards. What might help you to do this?**

- **A** Guessing
- **B** Instinct
- **C** Repetition
- **D** Trial and error

20 **Which of the following is not a way that you could become more active during your day?**

- **J** Take the elevator rather than the stairs.
- **K** Ride your bike to school instead of the bus.
- **L** Go for a walk instead of watching TV.
- **M** Walk to the store rather than driving.

Answer Keys

ITBS

Grade 6 ITBS Answer Keys

Question Number	Correct Answer	Code/ Objective
Unit One		
1	A	Science-01
2	J	Science-01
3	D	Science-03
4	L	Science-01
5	C	Science-01
6	M	Science-01
7	A	Science-04
8	K	Science-04
9	D	Science-04
10	J	Science-04
11	D	Science-01
12	L	Science-01
13	B	Science-04
14	L	Science-01
15	B	Science-04
16	M	Science-01
17	B	Science-04
18	J	Science-01
19	C	Science-04

Question Number	Correct Answer	Code/ Objective
Unit Two		
1	C	Science-02
2	M	Science-02
3	D	Science-02
4	L	Science-02
5	C	Science-02
6	K	Science-02
7	C	Science-02
8	M	Science-01
9	B	Science-02
10	J	Science-01
11	B	Science-01
12	L	Science-02
13	D	Science-02
14	K	Science-02
15	C	Science-02
16	K	Science-02
17	D	Science-01
18	J	Science-01
19	D	Science-02
20	J	Science-02

Grade 6 ITBS Answer Keys

Question Number	Correct Answer	Code/ Objective
Unit Three		
1	C	Science-01
2	L	Science-01
3	C	Science-04
4	J	Science-04
5	D	Science-04
6	M	Science-03
7	A	Science-04
8	L	Science-01
9	B	Science-01
10	L	Science-04
11	D	Science-04
12	J	Science-04
13	B	Science-04
14	L	Science-04
15	A	Science-04
16	K	Science-01
17	B	Science-03
18	J	Science-01
19	B	Science-01

Question Number	Correct Answer	Code/ Objective
Unit Four		
1	C	Science-01
2	J	Science-03
3	C	Science-01
4	K	Science-03
5	B	Science-03
6	J	Science-03
7	B	Science-01
8	J	Science-03
9	C	Science-03
10	L	Science-01
11	D	Science-01
12	K	Science-03
13	A	Science-01
14	L	Science-03
15	D	Science-01
16	L	Science-03
17	A	Science-03
18	K	Science-01
19	C	Science-03
20	K	Science-03
21	D	Science-01

Grade 6 ITBS Answer Keys

Question Number	Correct Answer	Code/ Objective
Unit Five		
1	C	Science-03
2	K	Science-03
3	D	Science-03
4	M	Science-03
5	A	Science-03
6	L	Science-03
7	A	Science-03
8	K	Science-03
9	C	Science-01
10	J	Science-03
11	C	Science-03
12	M	Science-03
13	A	Science-01
14	L	Science-01
15	A	Science-01
16	K	Science-01
17	C	Science-01
18	K	Science-03
19	C	Science-03

Question Number	Correct Answer	Code/ Objective
Unit Six		
1	B	Science-02
2	M	Science-02
3	B	Science-02
4	L	Science-01
5	B	Science-01
6	K	Science-01
7	A	Science-02
8	L	Science-01
9	A	Science-01
10	M	Science-01
11	B	Science-01
12	J	Science-01
13	C	Science-02
14	M	Science-02
15	B	Science-02
16	L	Science-03
17	B	Science-03
18	M	Science-02
19	C	Science-02
20	J	Science-02

Grade 6 ITBS Answer Keys

Question Number	Correct Answer	Code/ Objective
Unit Seven		
1	C	Science-02
2	K	Science-02
3	B	Science-02
4	L	Science-02
5	B	Science-01
6	M	Science-02
7	C	Science-02
8	K	Science-02
9	C	Science-01
10	J	Science-01
11	B	Science-02
12	L	Science-02
13	B	Science-02
14	L	Science-02
15	B	Science-02
16	M	Science-02
17	A	Science-02
18	K	Science-02
19	C	Science-02
20	J	Science-02

Stanford 9

Stanford 9
Stanford 9
Stanford 9

WHAT DO I NEED TO KNOW ABOUT THE SAT-9 SCIENCE SECTION?

The Stanford Achievement Test (also know as the Stanford 9 or the SAT-9) covers many other subjects besides science. Your students will probably also take the language arts, mathematics, and social studies sections of the SAT-9. This workbook prepares your students for the types of *science* questions they will see on the SAT-9.

In the sixth grade, students usually take the Intermediate 2 or Intermediate 3 level of the SAT-9. They must take the Complete Battery version in order to have a science section. Ask your school's test coordinator or principal to find out if your students will take the Complete Battery. Also ask if they will take the Intermediate 2 or Intermediate 3 level of the test.

If students take Intermediate 2 or Intermediate 3, they will have 40 questions to answer in 25 minutes. These numbers are based on Form S, and other forms vary slightly.

The SAT-9 also offers open-ended science assessments that may be used in addition to or instead of the usual multiple-choice versions.

The SAT-9 is a norm-referenced test, which means that it can be used to compare one group of students to another. On each student's score report, there will be a percentile score that shows how she has performed compared to other students at the same grade level. However, technically, the student is not being compared to *all* students at that grade level across the country. She is only compared to the group of students that was in the norm group—a group that *represents* all students at that grade level across the country.

Because the SAT-9 is a national test, its science questions are not based on any one state or district's science curriculum. This means that the SAT-9 asks very general science questions. Students must understand general science concepts in order to do well, but they do not need to know many specific factual details.

More so than the TerraNova or ITBS, the SAT-9 uses pictures, tables, and graphs to provide students with information that they must interpret in order to answer questions. Make sure that your students know how to use these graphics and can pay close attention to details in them.

Notice also that students have far less than a minute per question for the science section. The science section of the SAT-9 requires students to work faster than the TerraNova or ITBS. Be sure to provide some timed practice with the unit tests. When deciding how much time to allow for a unit test, estimate about 35–40 seconds per question.

The list of "content and process clusters" on page 51 shows the broad areas of science knowledge that are covered on the SAT-9.

SAT-9 Science Content and Process Clusters for Grade 6

Each objective is followed by the code used in the answer key to indicate which questions in the unit tests are associated with it.

Earth and Space Science (Earth Science)

These questions ask about the Solar System and Earth's geology, weather, and history.

Physical Science (Physical Science)

These questions ask about forces, motion, energy, and matter. They require students to understand basic changes.

Life Science (Life Science)

These questions deal with living organisms and ecosystems. Students must be able to answer questions about common functions of various parts of plants and animals, and have basic knowledge of their interactions.

Using Evidence and Models (Science-01)

These questions test students' familiarity with the processes of scientific investigation. They require students to be familiar with the common purposes and methods of scientific experiments. Students must also be familiar with charts, tables, and other graphic representations of data.

Recognizing Constancy and Patterns of Change (Science-02)

These questions require students to use information presented to compare and contrast.

Comparing Form and Function (Science-03)

These questions require students to understand the relationship between what something is and what it does.

WHAT DO MY STUDENTS NEED TO KNOW ABOUT THE SAT-9?

The following approaches can help students before the actual SAT-9 administration.

Ease Students' Minds while Motivating Them

- Let students know that the SAT-9 is not a test of how smart they are. It is a test that lets them show the skills and facts they have learned in class, and what they have yet to learn.
- Emphasize that the SAT-9 will not affect students' grades, but that they should do their best because the test is important in a different way. It helps show what they've learned over this year and previous years.

Give Students the Facts about the Test

- Explain the difference between standardized tests and classroom tests. Point out the importance of each kind of test.
- Explain to students that they will probably come across some questions that are difficult for them to answer. They may even see a question that requires a skill or fact they have not learned at all. This test is designed to have some very difficult questions, so they should not get discouraged. All students will have trouble with some questions.
- Check to be sure that your students must take the Complete Battery version of the SAT-9. Find out which level of the test they will take: Intermediate 2 or Intermediate 3. Tell them how many science questions there will be and how much time they will have, according to the information on page 50. Let them know that there will also be math, reading, writing, and social studies questions in separate sections.
- Find out from the test coordinator at your school how many days your students will have to take all of the SAT-9 sections. Reassure students that they will have more than one day to take the test.

Familiarize Students with the Testing Situation

- Remind students that standardized tests are not group activities, so they will have to work alone.
- If students are not used to using a separate answer sheet, be sure to explain this process and provide some practice using one in advance of the real test. The answer sheet on page 54 can help you do this.
- The SAT-9 is a timed test, so students should work carefully and not allow themselves to get stuck on any one question. Working carefully but steadily, only some students will be able to answer all of the questions. Students should get as far as they can.
- Try to determine which students feel anxious about the test and which are overconfident. Some students need to be reassured about their abilities, while

Provide Basic Test-taking Tips for the SAT-9

- ✔ Listen to all of the directions the teacher reads aloud.
- ✔ Read all directions in the test booklet carefully.
- ✔ Read each question and answer choice carefully. Always read all of the choices.
- ✔ Examine any graphics that accompany the question.
- ✔ Use your time wisely and don't get stuck on one question.
- ✔ Use the process of elimination. (See page 6 for one way to introduce the process of elimination to students in class.)
- ✔ Answer each question, even when you have not narrowed down the choices to just one.
- ✔ If you have only a few minutes left and many questions to answer, continue working steadily and answer any questions for which you can eliminate at least one answer choice.

Provide Tips for Answering Questions with Graphics

Most questions in the SAT-9 science section include graphics. We have included these types of questions in the unit tests so that students can practice the skills they will need to do well on the SAT-9.

The following types of graphics appear on the SAT-9:

- maps
- tables
- flow charts
- bar graphs
- line graphs
- pie graphs
- diagrams
- sequenced pictures and text
- pictures showing various experimental situations
- pictures of items that need to be compared

Review maps, tables, flow charts, and graphs regularly with students to be sure they are familiar with how to interpret all of them. Be sure that they pay attention to the "fine print," like the titles, labels, and keys.

For any question involving a diagram or picture, instruct students to do the following:

1. Look closely at the details. You can get a lot of information from very small parts of the drawings on the SAT-9. They are not in color, so you may not find them very interesting to look at, but you must learn to look at them carefully.
2. If there is more than one picture, think about the differences between them.
3. If there is text, read it all. Think about how it is related to the pictures. Be sure to understand which labels apply to the entire picture and which apply to just parts of it.
4. Decide if there is any sort of order to the way the pictures and text are arranged. Are they in time order? Are they just meant to be compared?
5. If you prefer to think in words, then name the things or organisms that you see before answering the question.

Name: ______________________________ **Date:** ______________

Unit Number: ______________________

1	Ⓐ	Ⓑ	Ⓒ	Ⓓ	14	Ⓕ	Ⓖ	Ⓗ	Ⓙ
2	Ⓕ	Ⓖ	Ⓗ	Ⓙ	15	Ⓐ	Ⓑ	Ⓒ	Ⓓ
3	Ⓐ	Ⓑ	Ⓒ	Ⓓ	16	Ⓕ	Ⓖ	Ⓗ	Ⓙ
4	Ⓕ	Ⓖ	Ⓗ	Ⓙ	17	Ⓐ	Ⓑ	Ⓒ	Ⓓ
5	Ⓐ	Ⓑ	Ⓒ	Ⓓ	18	Ⓕ	Ⓖ	Ⓗ	Ⓙ
6	Ⓕ	Ⓖ	Ⓗ	Ⓙ	19	Ⓐ	Ⓑ	Ⓒ	Ⓓ
7	Ⓐ	Ⓑ	Ⓒ	Ⓓ	20	Ⓕ	Ⓖ	Ⓗ	Ⓙ
8	Ⓕ	Ⓖ	Ⓗ	Ⓙ	21	Ⓐ	Ⓑ	Ⓒ	Ⓓ
9	Ⓐ	Ⓑ	Ⓒ	Ⓓ	22	Ⓕ	Ⓖ	Ⓗ	Ⓙ
10	Ⓕ	Ⓖ	Ⓗ	Ⓙ	23	Ⓐ	Ⓑ	Ⓒ	Ⓓ
11	Ⓐ	Ⓑ	Ⓒ	Ⓓ	24	Ⓕ	Ⓖ	Ⓗ	Ⓙ
12	Ⓕ	Ⓖ	Ⓗ	Ⓙ	25	Ⓐ	Ⓑ	Ⓒ	Ⓓ
13	Ⓐ	Ⓑ	Ⓒ	Ⓓ					

Name: ______________________ Date: ____________

Unit One

Read each question and choose the best answer. Mark your answer on your answer sheet.

1 **Which of the following is a physical property?**

A Volume

B Size

C Density

D Mass

2

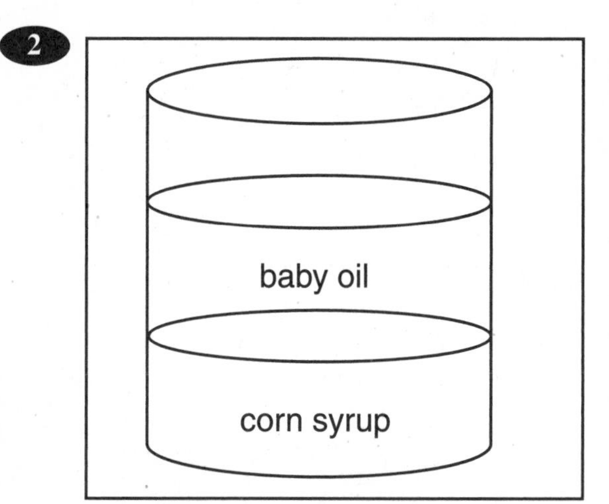

Water is less dense than corn syrup but more dense than baby oil. When a sample of water is added to the glass, it will probably end up —

F above the baby oil

G beneath the corn syrup

H mixing into the baby oil layer

J in between the baby oil and corn syrup

3

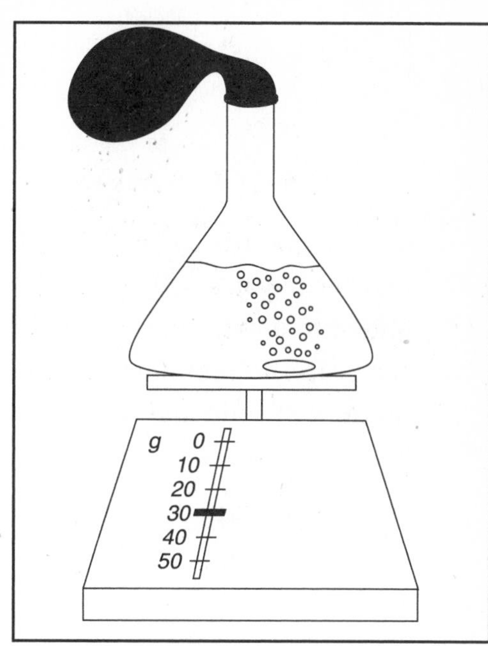

When the chemical change in the test tube is finished, the scale should read —

A where it was at the beginning of the experiment

B higher than at the beginning of the experiment

C lower than at the beginning of the experiment

D equal to zero

4 **When litmus paper is dipped into a mystery substance, it turns blue. Which of these could be the mystery substance?**

F Lemon juice

G Battery acid

H Soap

J Vinegar

Name: ______________________ Date: ____________

5

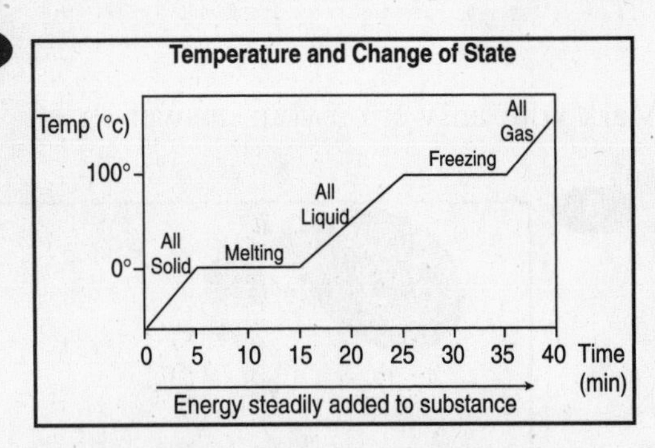

The temperature of a solid substance is recorded as energy is steadily added to it over time. According to the graph, what time is the sample a mixture of solid and liquid?

A 2 minutes

B 10 minutes

C 20 minutes

D 30 minutes

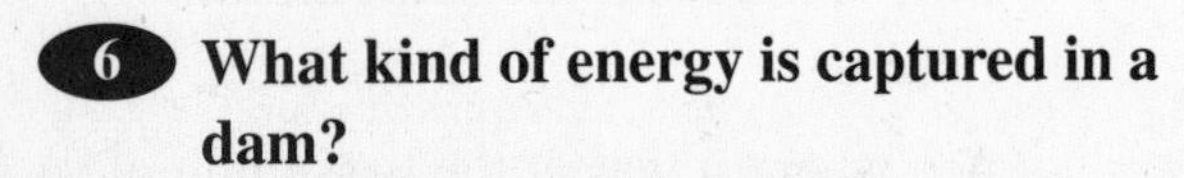

6 What kind of energy is captured in a dam?

F Solar energy from the Sun

G Fossil fuels

H Nuclear energy from Earth's core

J Potential energy in stored water

7

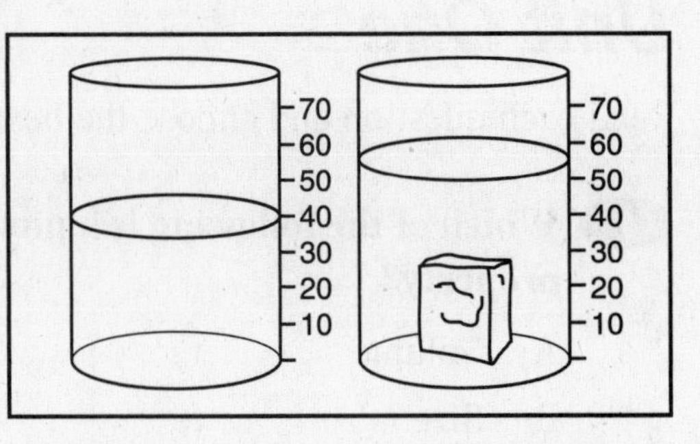

What is the volume of the block that was dropped into the beaker of water?

A 40 ml

B 55 ml

C 15 ml

D 25 ml

8

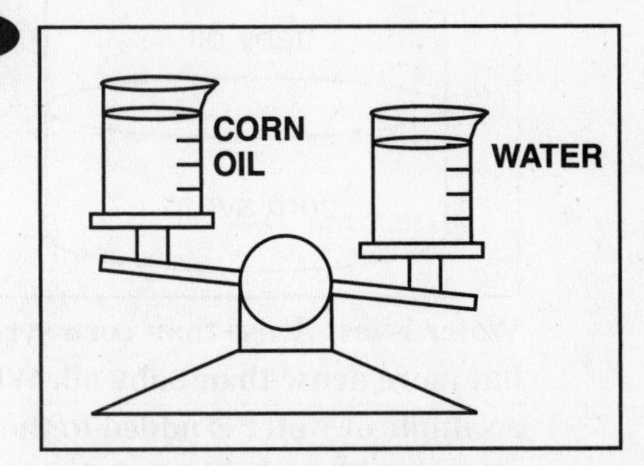

What can be concluded about corn oil and water from looking at the picture?

F Corn oil and water have the same density.

G Corn oil is more dense than water.

H Corn oil weighs more than water.

J Water is more dense than corn oil.

9 At room temperature, oxygen is a —

A gas

B liquid

C solid

D solution

Name: ______________________ Date: ____________

10 **Which of the following is *not* a physical change?**

F Water boiling

G Wood burning

H Ice melting

J Cutting cloth

11 **A person floats better in water if he or she takes a deep breath. What is the most likely reason for this?**

A Taking a deep breath pushes water away from you.

B Taking a deep breath makes a person more dense.

C Taking a deep breath makes a person weigh more.

D Taking a deep breath makes a person less dense.

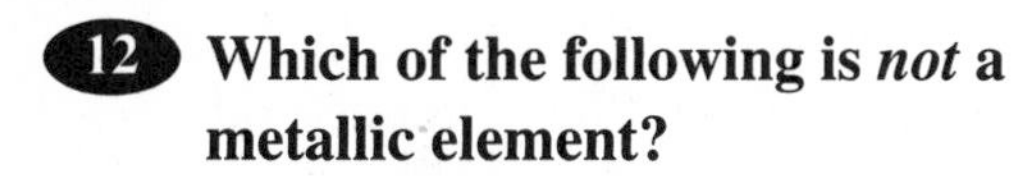

12 **Which of the following is *not* a metallic element?**

F Chlorine

G Aluminum

H Iron

J Copper

13

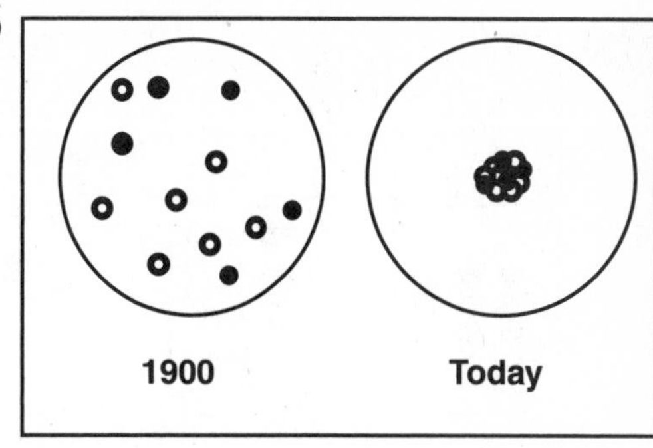

The picture shows what scientists thought was inside an atom one hundred years ago and what they think is inside an atom today. How has their thinking changed?

A Scientists used to think that the parts of an atom were all packed in the center, but now they think that they are spread all over the atom.

B Scientists used to think that atoms were empty, but now they think that they are full of smaller parts.

C Scientists used to think that the parts of atoms were lined up inside the atom, but now they think that they are packed in the middle of the atom.

D Scientists used to think the parts of an atom were spread all over the atom, but now they think that they are packed in the center of the atom.

Name: ____________________ Date: ____________

14

Solid Liquid Gas

Melting Boiling

How is a gas different from a solid?

F Gas particles are packed tightly together, but solid particles move quickly.

G Solid particles move faster than gas particles.

H Solid particles are closer together than gas particles.

J Gas particles are colder than solid particles.

15 **What will litmus paper do when it is dipped into a glass containing acid rain?**

A Turn blue

B Turn red

C Turn yellow

D Turn green

16

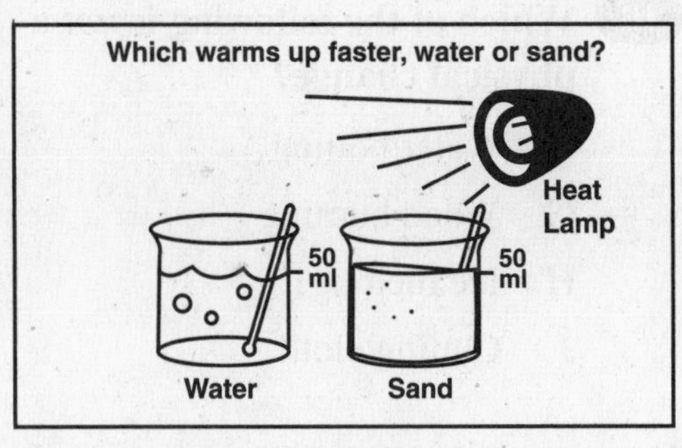

What is wrong with the way this experiment is designed?

F The water container should have more water in it.

G There shouldn't be any heat lamp.

H The heat lamp should be the same distance from the sand and water.

J There should be only one thermometer.

17 **What do scientists look for when creating a material to use as insulation?**

A Something that is expensive

B Something that is not a good conductor of heat

C Something that lets heat escape through it

D Something that melts easily

18 **Two balloons were blown up to be the same size. One was held down in a container of hot water. The other was held down in a container of cold water. What happened?**

F Both balloons popped.

G The balloon in cold water got larger than the balloon in hot water.

H The balloons stayed the same size.

J The balloon in hot water got larger than the balloon in cold water.

Name: ______________________ Date: ____________

Unit Two

Read each question and choose the best answer. Mark your answer on your answer sheet.

1 **Which of these is *not* found in an animal cell?**

A Nucleus

B Mitochondrion

C Chloroplast

D Cell membrane

2

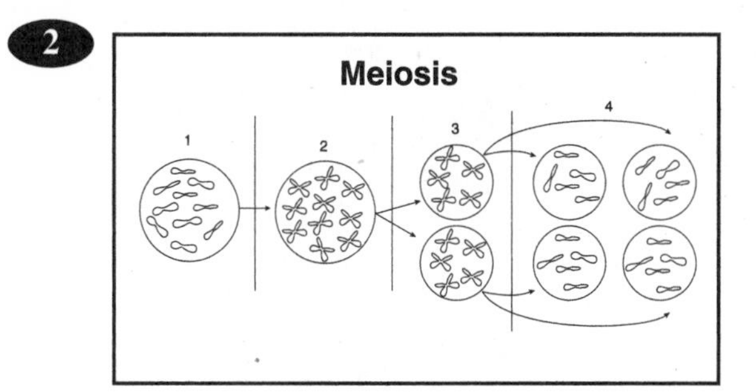

A cell about to go through meiosis contains 10 chromosomes in its nucleus. How many chromosomes will there be in the cells at the end of this process?

F 10

G 20

H 5

J 1

3 **A scientist performs research on how cell growth is controlled. Her findings might help to find a cure for —**

A AIDS

B baldness

C heart attacks

D cancer

4 **Which of the pictures is not a member of the phylum Chordata (the vertebrates)?**

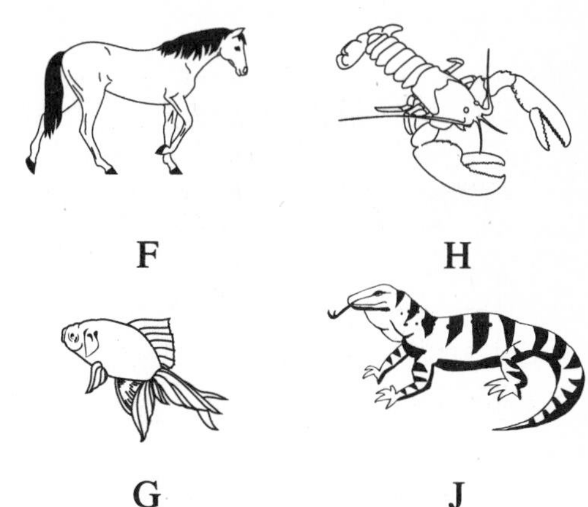

5

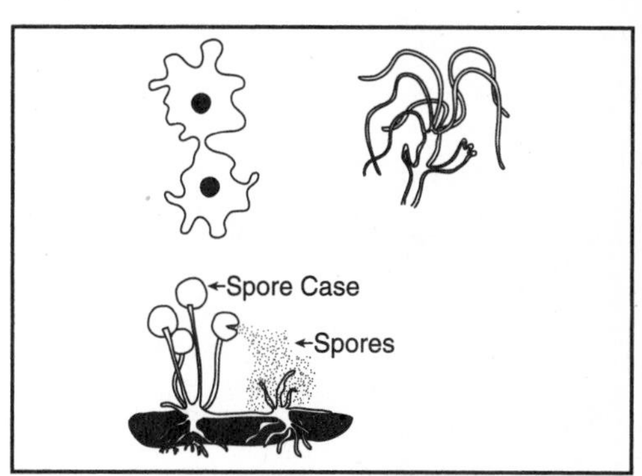

All of the organisms shown in the pictures are demonstrating which process?

A Spore production

B Reproduction

C Eating

D Competition

6 **Which is *not* a characteristic that all living things share?**

F Ability to grow

G Ability to make food from sunlight

H Ability to reproduce

J Ability to respond to the surroundings

Stanford 9 • Unit Two

Name: ______________________________ Date: ____________

7 Which of the following is a one-celled organism?

A A human

B A tree

C An amoeba

D A lizard

8

ELEMENTS THAT MAKE UP THE HUMAN BODY		
Symbol	Element	Percent
O	Oxygen	65.0
C	Carbon	18.5
H	Hydrogen	9.5
N	Nitrogen	3.3
Ca	Calcium	1.5
P	Phosphorous	1.0
K	Potassium	0.4
S	Sulfur	0.3
Na	Sodium	0.2
Cl	Chlorine	0.2
Mg	Magnesium	0.1

How much of your body is made up of oxygen and carbon?

F 65%

G 18.5%

H 28%

J 83.5%

9

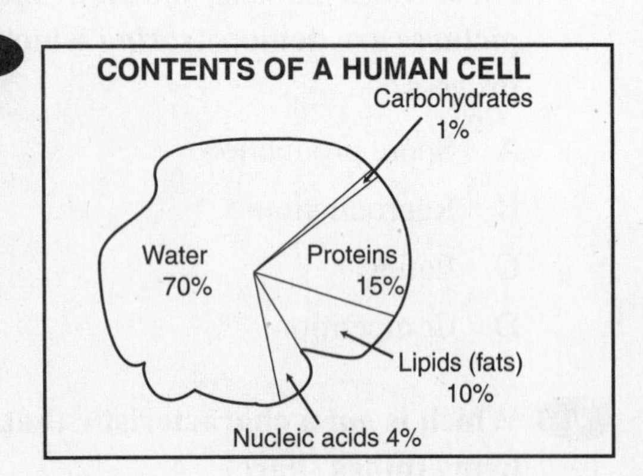

What percent of a human cell is *not* water?

A 70%

B 30%

C 15%

D 25%

10 Which invention allowed scientists to prove that all living things contain cells?

F The microscope

G The telescope

H The x-ray machine

J The computer

11

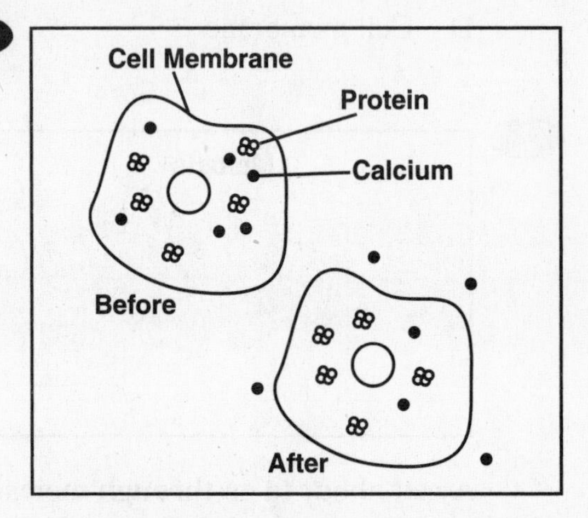

What does the picture tell you about the cell membrane?

A It lets anything move across it.

B Calcium can diffuse across it, but protein cannot.

C It lets only large molecules diffuse across it.

D Protein can diffuse across it, but calcium cannot.

12

Sunlight
Water
Carbon Dioxide → Photosynthesis → Sugar
→ Oxygen

Sugar
Oxygen
Respiration → Carbon Dioxide
→ ENERGY!
→ Water

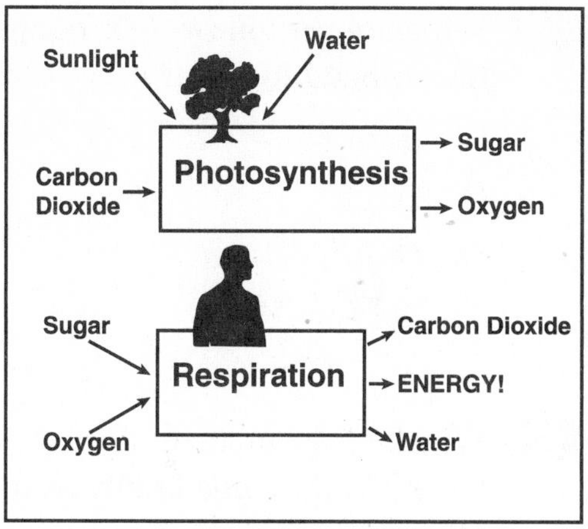

How do plants and animals use oxygen?

F Plants use oxygen during photosynthesis and animals make oxygen during respiration.

G Plants make oxygen during respiration and animals use oxygen during photosynthesis.

H Plants make oxygen during photosynthesis and animals use oxygen during respiration.

J Plants use oxygen during respiration and animals make oxygen during photosynthesis.

13 Which of the following is a fungus?

A Pine tree

B Amoeba

C Clam

D Mushroom

14 What do all members of the plant kingdom have in common?

F All plants are herbivores.

G All plants make their own food.

H All plants move from one place to another.

J All plants are vertebrates.

15 What word should go in the empty space in the table?

ANIMALS WITH BACKBONES	
Animal Class	Outer Covering
Birds	Feathers
Reptiles	Dry Scales
Fish	Wet Scales
Mammals	

A Fins

B Shells

C Body hair

D Milk

Name: ____________________ **Date:** ____________

16 **Why do tomato plants produce seeds inside the tomato?**

F To make the tomato taste better

G To reproduce and make more tomato plants

H To help the plant make food from the Sun

J To make the tomatoes grow faster

17

	Apple Juice	Apple Juice	Apple Juice	Apple Juice
What was done:	Boiled then covered	Frozen	Salt added then covered	Left on window in science room
What happened:	Juice is still clear	Juice is still clear	Juice is still clear	Juice is cloudy with bacteria

A science class performs an experiment to test what keeps bacteria from growing in apple juice. They did different things to containers of apple juice and then checked them three days later. What can be concluded from the results?

A Boiling keeps bacteria from growing, but freezing doesn't.

B Salt is the only way to keep bacteria from growing in apple juice.

C Bacteria can't grow in apple juice.

D Bacteria will grow in apple juice if it is left alone.

18 **Which of the following is *not* part of the animal life cycle?**

F Birth

G Death

H Growing

J Walking

19 **Which of the pictures does *not* belong in the same family as the others?**

A

C

B

D

Name: ______________________ Date: __________

Unit Three

Read each question and choose the best answer. Mark your answer on your answer sheet.

1

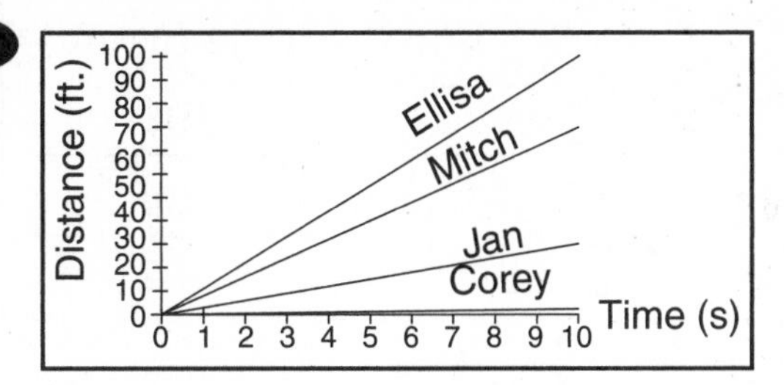

Which runner is traveling at the highest speed?

A Jan

B Mitch

C Ellisa

D Corey

2 **Which of the following describes both the speed and direction an object is moving?**

F Velocity

G Rate

H Acceleration

J Inertia

3

Time Interval	Distance Traveled (cm)
During 1st Second	5
During 2nd Second	10
During 3rd Second	20
During 4th Second	40

As a car rolls down a track, two students measure how far it travels during each second of its trip. During the trip, the car —

A traveled at constant speed

B lost velocity

C accelerated

D decelerated

4 **Which surface would exert the least friction force on your feet as you walk?**

F Ice

G Rug

H Sidewalk

J Grass

5 **Which of the following is a lubricant?**

A Sandpaper

B Wedge

C Oil

D Screw

Name: ______________________ Date: __________

6 **Which picture shows a lever?**

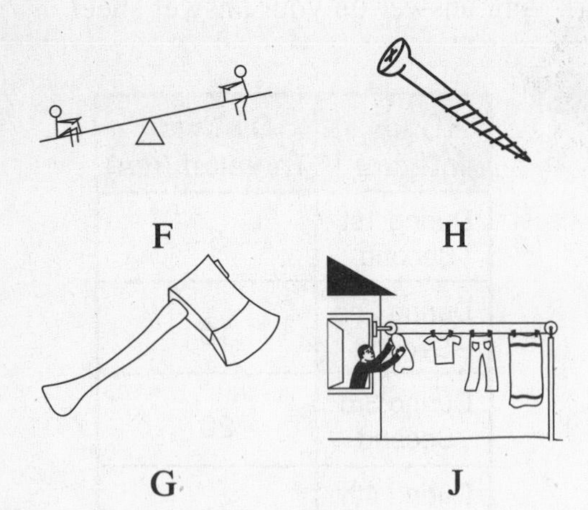

7

47th Street
Entrance
City Park
Pond
Parking Lot
Playground
N W E S

Jan parks in the parking lot of the city park and walks to the playground. Which direction is she walking?

A North

B South

C East

D West

8 **When a car's speed gets faster and faster, it is called —**

F acceleration

G position

H gravity

J friction

Use the following chart to answer questions 9 and 10.

Slope of ramp (in degrees)	Distance ball rolls (in cm)
45	105
35	84
25	62

9 **What can be concluded about balls rolling down ramps from this experiment?**

A The steeper the slope, the shorter the distance the ball rolls.

B The heavier the ball, the shorter the distance the ball rolls.

C The steeper the slope, the further the distance the ball rolls.

D The steepness of the slope doesn't affect how far the ball rolls.

10 **What would be the most likely distance the ball would roll after going down a ramp with a 15-degree slope?**

F 0 cm

G 45 cm

H 95 cm

J 125 cm

11 **A bike slows down when its brakes rub against its wheel. What kind of force is being applied to the wheel by the brakes?**

A Acceleration

B Centripetal

C Friction

D Potential

12 **When a ball is thrown up into the air, what makes it come back down again?**

F Air pressure

G Wind

H Speed

J Gravity

13 **Scientists have tried to design airplanes so that they move through the air as easily as possible. They design boats so that they move through water as easily as possible. What kind of force causes airplanes and boats to slow down as they move forward?**

A Drag force

B Weight

C Balanced force

D Newton

14 **The heavier a moving object is, the more momentum it has. Which object has the most momentum?**

F A bike going 5 miles per hour

G A school bus going 5 miles per hour

H A person running 5 miles per hour

J A small car going 5 miles per hour

15 **Which object has the most kinetic energy?**

A A bowling ball rolling 5 ft/s

B A golf ball rolling 5 ft/s

C A bowling ball rolling 20 ft/s

D A golf ball rolling 20 ft/s

16 **How do batteries make a radio work?**

F The battery has stored energy in it that can be changed into electricity.

G The battery has stored sounds in it that come out the radio speakers.

H The battery takes energy from the radio to make it work.

J The chemicals move from the battery into the radio to make sound.

Name: ____________________ Date: ____________

17

When Mary lets go of her pendulum, what will happen when the pendulum swings back toward her?

A The ball will go higher and higher with each swing.

B The ball will not go as high after each swing.

C The ball will go back to the same height after each swing.

D The ball will stop after one swing.

18 **Many countries use coal, natural gas, and oil as sources of energy for motor vehicles and electricity. What does it mean to conserve these natural sources of energy?**

F To sell as much of them as possible

G To use as little as necessary because they might run out

H To trade them with other countries around the world

J To try to discover more of these energy sources in the ground

19

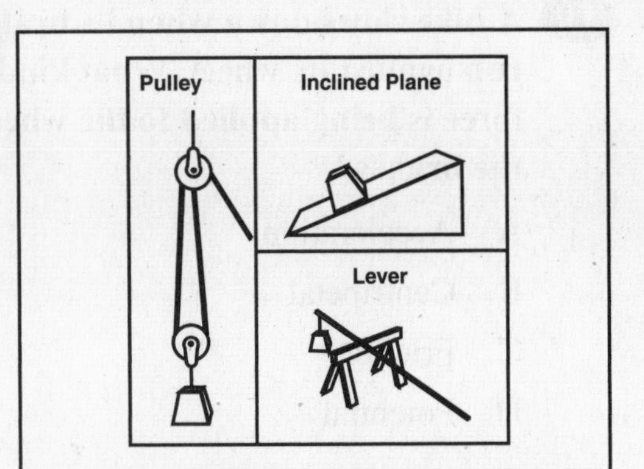

What do all of these simple machines have in common?

A They all make it easier to do work.

B They all make it harder to do work.

C They all work without any friction.

D They all have many parts.

20

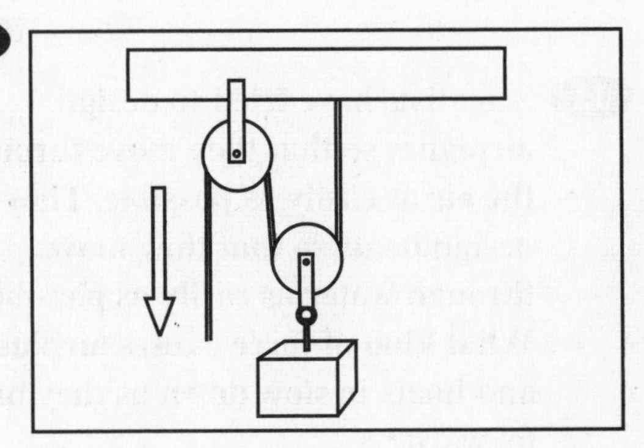

When Sean pulls down on the pulley rope, what will happen?

F The block will go down.

G The block will go up.

H The block will not move.

J The block will move to the left.

Name: ______________________ Date: __________

Unit Four

Read each question and choose the best answer. Mark your answer on your answer sheet.

1 **When it is summer in North America, what season is it in South America?**

A Summer

B Winter

C Spring

D Fall

2

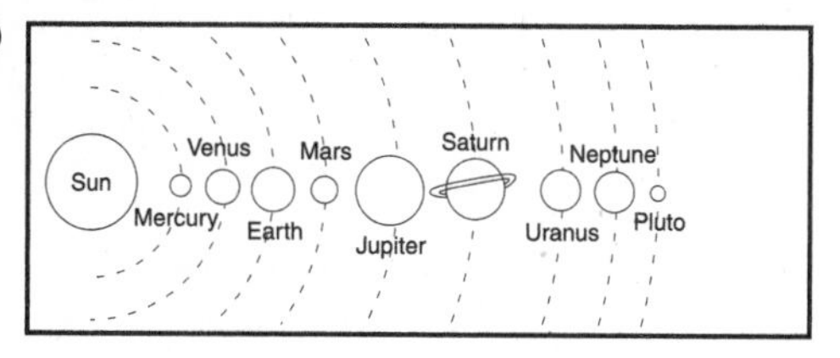

A year on a planet is the time it takes that planet to go around the Sun once. Which planet has the shortest year?

F Pluto

G Mercury

H Earth

J Saturn

3 **Which of these gives off its own light?**

A Saturn

B Star

C Moon

D Jupiter

4 **Instead of moving in straight lines, the planets orbit the Sun. What causes this?**

F Gravity of the Sun

G Inertia

H The other planets

J The Moon

5

PLANET	DIAMETER (km)
Earth	12,600
Jupiter	140,000
Mars	6,700
Mercury	4,830
Neptune	44,200
Pluto	6,000
Saturn	117,000
Uranus	46,000
Venus	12,100

Which is the largest planet in our solar system?

A Uranus

B Pluto

C Jupiter

D Sun

Name: ______________________________ Date: ______________

6 **Which instrument would be most useful for learning more about the planet Mars?**

F Microscope

G Telescope

H Magnifying glass

J X-ray machine

7 **When NASA wants to send astronauts into space to do experiments and then bring them back when the experiments are done, they use a —**

A space shuttle

B star

C satellite

D missle

8 **Water used by the astronauts is purified and reused. Why do they need to recycle water in a spacecraft?**

F Because they can collect water from outer space

G Because they need water to power the spacecraft

H Because they can only bring small amounts of water with them

J Because they need to breathe water vapor

9

PAST SPACE MISSIONS

Year	Spacecraft	Carrying Crew?	Mission
1958	Explorer III	No	Discovered Earth's radiation belt
1966	Surveyor I	No	First American soft landing on Moon's surface
1969	Apollo 11	Yes	First landing by humans on the Moon
1972	Pioneer 10	No	Flew by and took pictures of Jupiter
1990	Hubble Space Telescope	No	Took pictures of stars and collision of comet with Jupiter
1996	Mars Pathfinder	No	Sent remote-controlled car to take pictures of surface of Mars

Why was the Hubble Space Telescope sent into space?

A To land on the Moon

B To land on Mars and take pictures

C To fly by Jupiter

D To take pictures of stars and planets

10 **If you are walking and your shadow is stretched out in front of you, where is the Sun?**

F In front of you

G Behind you

H On your left side

J Directly overhead

Name: ______________________ Date: __________

11 Which picture shows the correct shadow pattern for the pencil at sunrise?

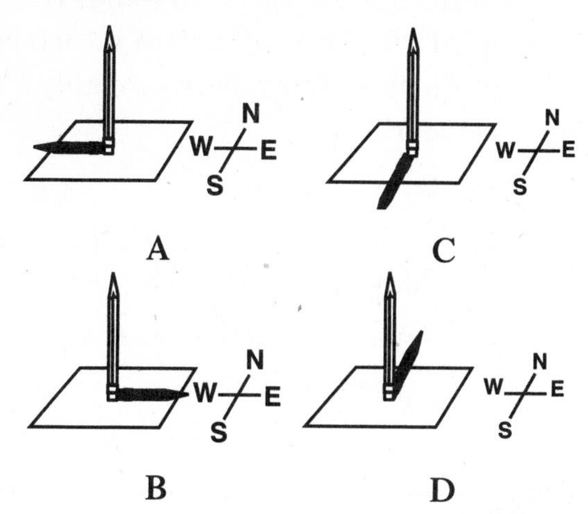

12

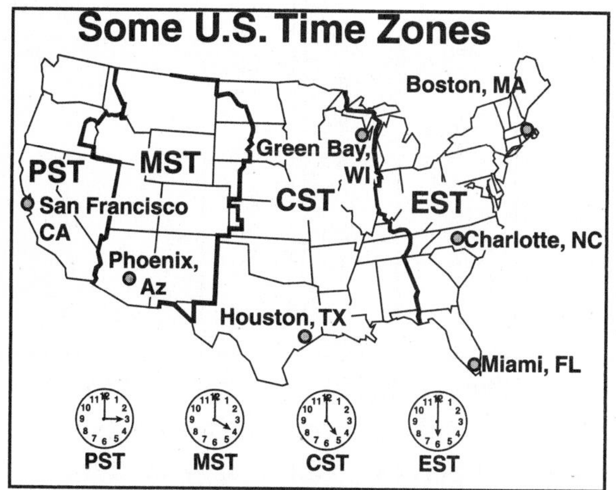

If it is 6:00 PM in Miami, FL, what time is it in San Francisco, CA?

F 9:00 PM

G 3:00 AM

H 3:00 PM

J 4:00 PM

13 Which of the following cities sees the sunrise first each day?

A San Francisco, CA

B Phoenix, AZ

C Green Bay, WI

D Boston, MA

14

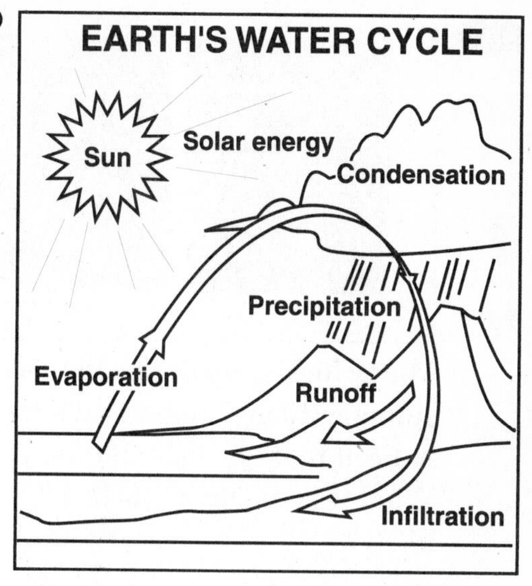

Which part of the water cycle uses the Sun as a source of energy to make it happen?

F Runoff

G Infiltration

H Evaporation

J Precipitation

15 The gravity of the Moon and the Sun pull on Earth's oceans, making them rise and fall along the shore. This is called —

A the tides

B an eclipse

C precipitation

D the seasons

Stanford 9 • Unit Four

Name: ______________________________ Date: ______________

16

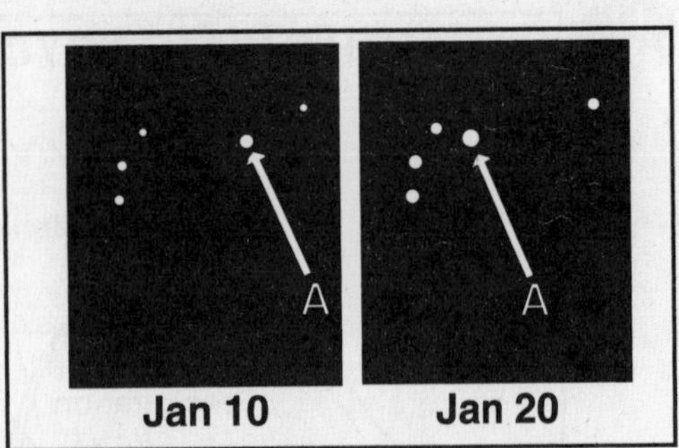

Marty looked up at the night sky on January 10 and January 20. He noticed that one light had moved. What was the light marked "A" most likely?

F An airplane

G A planet

H A space station

J A star

17 **Space probes sent to Mercury and Venus have sent back information that there are lava flows on both of these planets. What probably caused these lava flows?**

A Earthquakes

B Erosion from water

C Volcanoes on the planets' surfaces

D Space probes from Earth

18 **Earth's atmosphere has lots of oxygen in it but there is no oxygen in the atmospheres on Mercury, Venus, or Mars. Where did all of the oxygen in Earth's atmosphere probably come from?**

F Stars

G Plants on Earth giving off oxygen during photosynthesis

H Animals breathing out oxygen

J Outer space

19

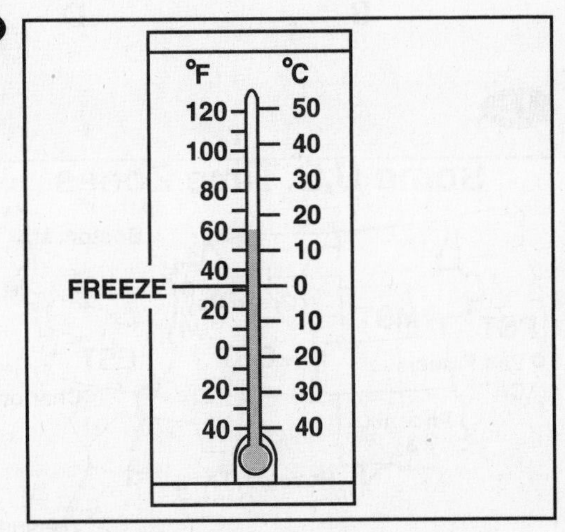

The alcohol in a thermometer expands and contracts when the temperature changes. What makes the alcohol rise?

A When it gets colder, the alcohol expands and moves up the tube.

B When it gets warmer, the alcohol contracts and moves down the tube.

C When it gets colder, more alcohol comes into the tube from the air.

D When it gets warmer, the alcohol expands and moves up the tube.

Name: ______________________ Date: ______________

Unit Five

Read each question and choose the best answer. Mark your answer on your answer sheet.

1 **Geologists believe that Earth's continents were bunched together millions of years ago. Slowly, Earth's crust has moved, spreading the continents apart as they are today. According to this theory, which is the oldest picture of Earth?**

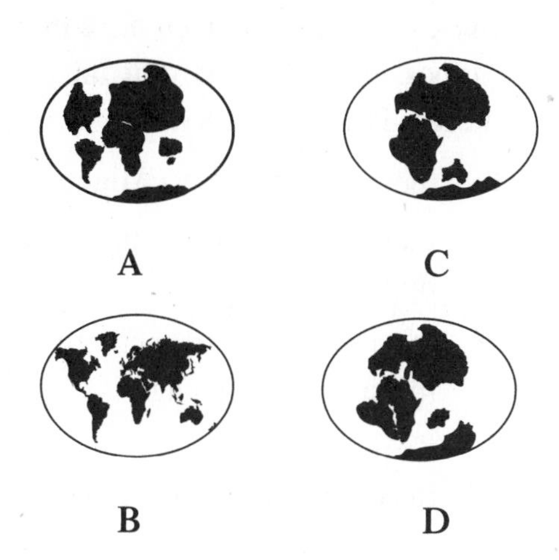

2 **A geologist is studying a canyon wall made of sedimentary rock. She can predict which layers are oldest because —**

F the top layers are usually the oldest

G the oldest layers are always granite

H the oldest layers are usually darkest in color

J the lowest layers are usually the oldest

3 **According to the picture, this volcano —**

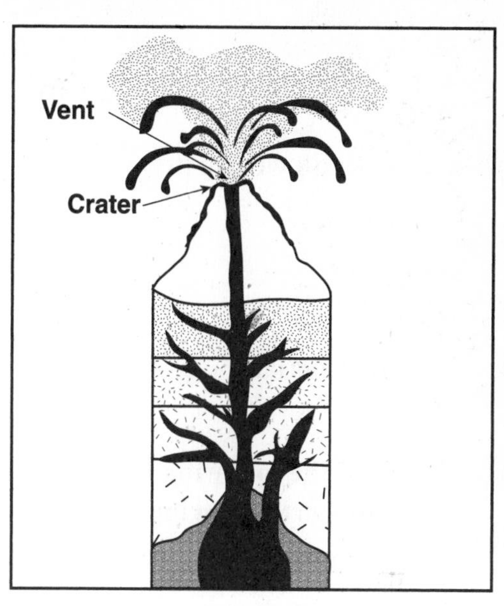

A is erupting for the first time

B has erupted only one other time

C has erupted many times

D is inactive

4 **In this power plant, energy is being changed from —**

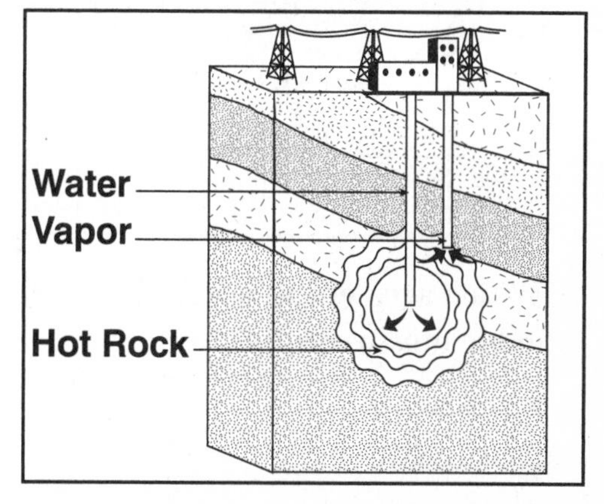

F chemical energy to heat energy

G heat energy to electrical energy

H mechanical energy to atomic energy

J electrical energy to heat energy

Stanford 9 • Unit Five

Name: ______________________________ Date: ______________

5 **Huge moving fields of ice are known as —**

A magma
B glaciers
C bedrock
D mantle

6 **What era do we live in?**

F Mesozoic
G Cenozoic
H Paleozoic
J Precambrian

7 **Which of the following is an example of Earth's crust moving?**

A Fossils
B Hurricanes
C Earthquakes
D Waves

8

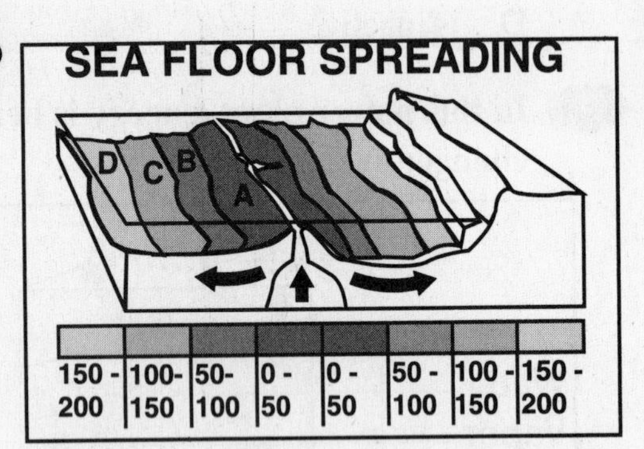

Which area of this ocean floor was made most recently?

F Area A
G Area B
H Area C
J Area D

9 **Which of the following is a natural resource that comes from Earth's crust?**

A Wood
B Coal
C Cloth
D Rain

10 **The west coast of Africa and the east coast of South America have matching shapes, almost like two fitting puzzle pieces. This suggests that —**

F there used to be no Atlantic Ocean
G they were eroded in the same way by the ocean
H they were next to each other millions of years ago
J there are the same animals living in Africa and South America

Name: ______________________ Date: ____________

11 **Fossils usually are of shells, bones, or teeth, because all of these parts —**

A are hard and last long enough to be preserved

B are soft and decay quickly

C are found in every living thing

D were found in ancient animals, but not in animals living today

12 **Which is *not* a technique to reduce soil erosion on farms?**

F Planting rows of trees to block the wind

G Keeping the soil dry and loose

H Planting strips of plants with deep roots

J Planting grass on large dirt fields

13 **When sedimentary rocks in the crust are exposed to heat and pressure, they can change into —**

A igneous rock

B sedimentary rock

C metamorphic rock

D humus

14 **Which is *not* a way that scientists divide minerals into categories?**

F By hardness

G By texture

H By structure

J By taste

15 **Soil with a lot of clay particles in it is usually impermeable, which means that —**

A it does not let water through

B it can hold lots of water in it

C it is impossible to dig through

D it has lots of large pores, or spaces, inside it

16

What happens to water when it freezes?

What can be concluded from this experiment about water when it freezes?

F Water changes into another liquid when it freezes.

G Water expands when it turns into ice.

H Water has a volume of 80 ml every time it freezes.

J Water contracts when it turns into ice.

Name: ______________________ Date: ____________

17 **When water seeps into the cracks in rocks and then freezes, what might happen?**

A The water may turn the rock into metamorphic rock.

B The ice may act as glue to seal the cracks permanently.

C The rocks may be broken apart when the water expands.

D The water will contract and pull the rock together at the cracks.

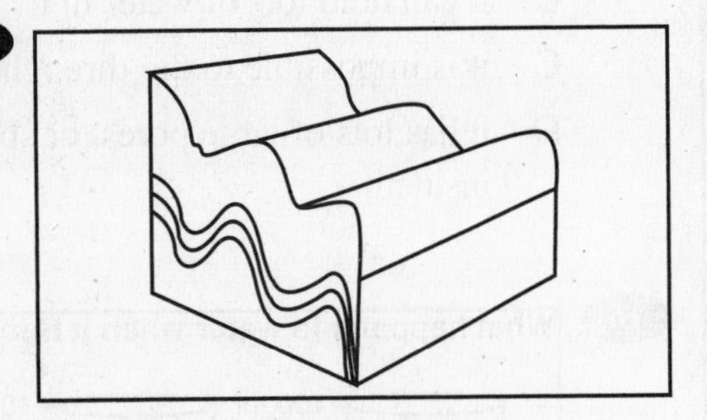

How do geologists believe fold mountains are formed?

F Rock layers are squeezed together as Earth's crust moves.

G Fold mountains are inactive volcanoes.

H Rock layers are tilted and broken apart.

J Earthquakes cause large cracks in Earth's crust.

19 **What does it mean when a volcano is dormant?**

A It is currently erupting.

B It is currently inactive, but erupted in the past.

C It has never erupted.

D It is a very small volcano that is currently erupting.

20 **In what areas of the world do architects build bridges and buildings with flexible materials?**

F Areas where volcanic eruptions are likely

G Areas that are very cold

H Areas where earthquakes are likely

J Areas where few people live

Name: ______________________ Date: ____________

Unit Six

Read each question and choose the best answer. Mark your answer on your answer sheet.

1 Heredity is the passing of characteristics on from parents to offspring. Which of these is an inherited trait?

A Where you live

B Your eye color

C Your age

D Your hair length

2

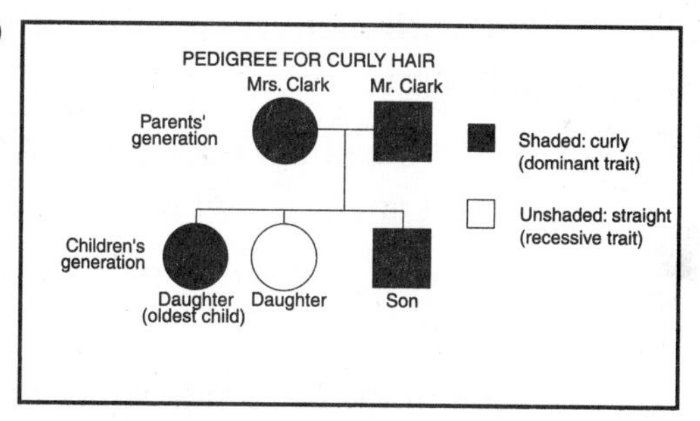

Mr. and Ms. Clark have three children. According to the chart, they have —

F two daughters with curly hair

G one son with curly hair

H one son with curly hair and one son with straight hair

J one son with straight hair

3 A genetic disorder is inherited from your parents. Which of these is a genetic disorder?

A Cystic fibrosis

B Chicken pox

C Influenza

D Sore throat

4

Chromosomes in Plant and Animal Cells

Human Rabbit Carrot Grasshopper

According to the picture —

F all species have their own numbers of chromosomes

G all species have the same number of chromosomes

H insects do not have chromosomes

J plant cells have more chromosomes than animal cells

5

IF YOU ARE BLOOD TYPE	YOU CAN RECEIVE TYPE	YOU CAN DONATE TO PEOPLE WITH TYPE
A	O, A	A, AB
B	O, B	B, AB
AB	O, A, B, AB	AB
O	O	A, B, AB, O

Georgette is in the hospital and needs someone to donate blood to her. Her blood type is B. Which kind(s) of blood can she receive?

A A and O

B B and O

C only B

D B and AB

Name: ______________________________ Date: ______________

6 **In 1997, scientists announced that they had created a sheep named Dolly who was a clone. The scientists had taken DNA from an adult sheep and used it to make Dolly. Because Dolly and the other sheep had the same DNA, they were identical. Many scientists are excited about cloning because —**

F there is a shortage of sheep around the world

G they might be able to clone human cells to replace damaged ones in patients

H they didn't know DNA carried inherited traits

J they want to use cloning to make many new kinds of sheep

7 **Without knowing it, bees that gather nectar from pea plant flowers are helping the pea plants to reproduce. How are they doing this?**

A They are eating the peas.

B They are carrying pollen that fertilizes the flowers.

C They are planting baby pea plants.

D They are helping the plants to photosynthesize.

8 **When pollen from purple pea plant flowers is used to fertilize white pea plant flowers, all of the offspring plants have purple flowers. In peas, purple is —**

F a dominant trait

G a recessive trait

H not an inherited trait

J an incompletely dominant trait

9

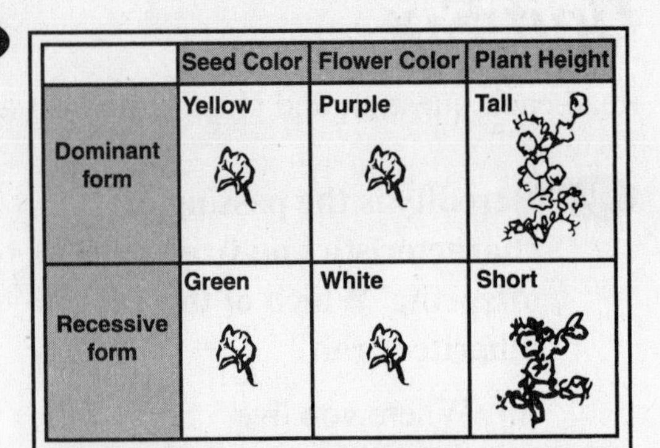

	Seed Color	Flower Color	Plant Height
Dominant form	Yellow	Purple	Tall
Recessive form	Green	White	Short

When purple and white pea plants are crossed, all of the offspring plants have purple flowers. What would you predict would happen when a tall plant is crossed with a short plant?

A Half the offspring plants will be short and half will be tall.

B All of the offspring plants will be short.

C All of the offspring plants will be tall.

D Half the offspring plants will be medium and half will be tall or short.

10 **Peter fills a bag with 50 red jelly beans and 50 black jelly beans. If he reaches into the bag to pull out a jelly bean, what is the chance that he'll pull out a black one?**

F 50%

G 1 out of 3

H 100%

J 1 out of 10

Name: ______________________ Date: __________

11 **Peter pulls out a jelly bean, records what color it is, and then puts it back. He repeats this 20 times. How many times did he probably get a red jelly bean?**

A 20

B 1

C 0

D 9

Use the information below to answer questions 12 and 13.

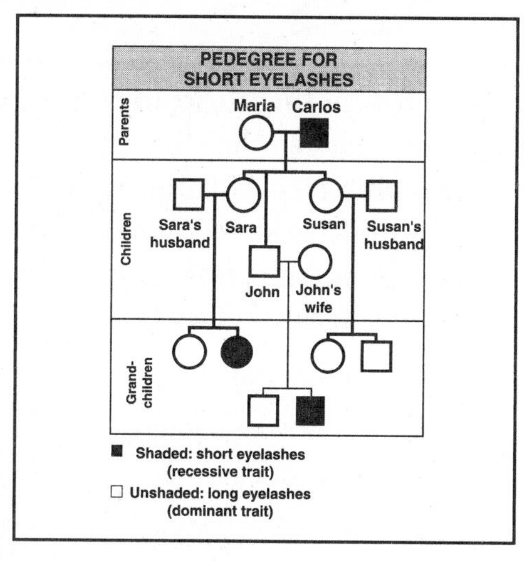

12 **How many grandsons with long eyelashes do Maria and Carlos have?**

F 1

G 2

H 0

J 3

13 **Sara and her husband have —**

A one daughter with long eyelashes and one daughter with short eyelashes

B one son with long eyelashes and one son with short eyelashes

C one daughter with long eyelashes and one son with long eyelashes

D one son with long eyelashes and one daughter with long eyelashes

14

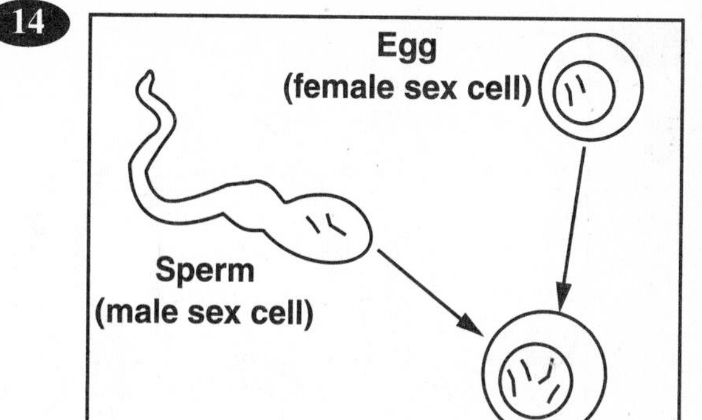

How does a fertilized egg get all of its chromosomes?

F All from the egg

G All from the sperm

H Half from the egg and half from the sperm

J One quarter from the sperm and three quarters from the egg

15 **What can be concluded from the chart about where a person's inherited traits come from?**

A A person's traits are mostly from the father.

B A person's traits are mostly from the mother.

C A person doesn't inherit any traits.

D A person's traits are a mixture from the mother and father.

16 **Many of a person's traits are inherited in her genes. A person's environment can also affect how she functions. Which of these is an example of an environmental affect?**

F Judy has blue eyes like her mother and father.

G Mark was paralyzed in a car accident.

H Juan is as tall as his father.

J Mike has two dimples like his grandmother and sister.

Name: ______________________ Date: ______________

17

Scientists believe that the woolly mammoth lived in North America more than a million years ago. What evidence do you think they have to support this theory?

A Books written back then

B Science fiction movies about woolly mammoths

C Fossils of woolly mammoth bones and tusks

D Pictures scientists found

18

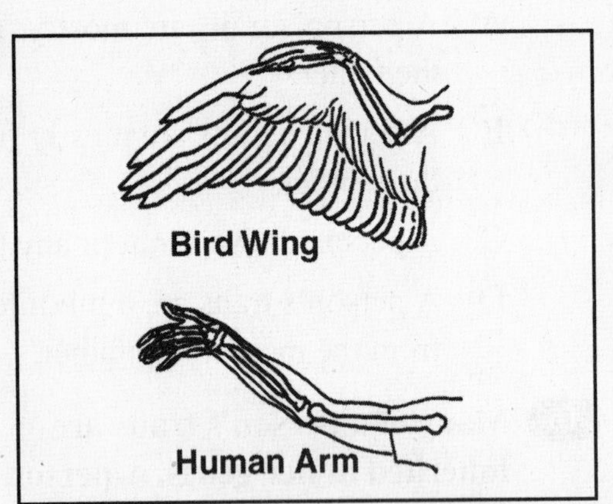

The bones in a bird's wing and a human's arm are similar in number and arrangement. This is evidence that —

F humans and birds are the same species

G humans can fly

H birds are more intelligent than humans

J humans and birds evolved from a common ancestor

19

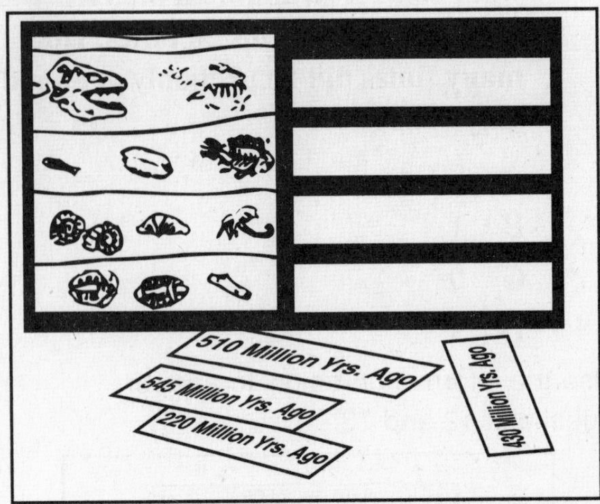

Scientists at the Museum of Natural History noticed that the labels have fallen off a display showing layers of fossils underground. Which of the labels should go on the bottom layer of fossils in the picture?

A 430 million years ago

B 545 million years ago

C 510 million years ago

D 220 million years ago

20 **Dinosaurs had dry, scaly skin, so they were probably most like today's —**

F fish

G mammals

H reptiles

J amphibians

Name: ______________________ Date: ______________

Unit Seven

Read each question and choose the best answer. Mark your answer on your answer sheet.

1 **Which of these is a reflex action?**

A Reading

B Blinking

C Jump-roping

D Talking

2

Endocrine Gland	Function In Body
pituitary gland	control over endocrine glands
thyroid gland	controls metabolism
parathyroid gland	controls level of calcium in blood
adrenal gland	controls water and salt in body

The endocrine glands are important organs in your body because they—

F keep the heart beating

G clean the blood of waste

H digest food

J help to control body processes and conditions

3

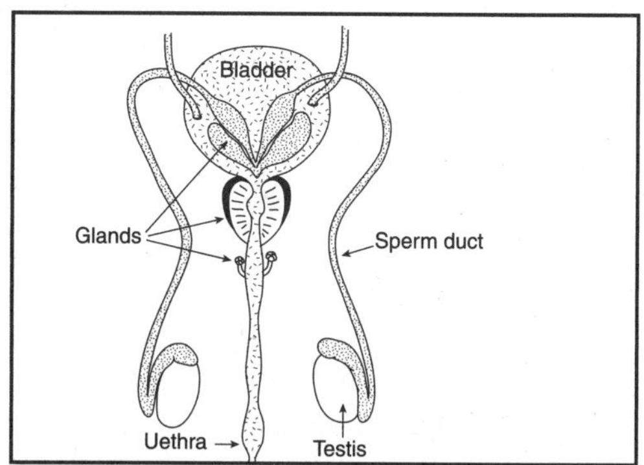

Which organ system of the body is in this picture?

A Nervous

B Respiratory

C Reproductive

D Circulatory

4 **Which animal reproduces by internal fertilization and gives birth to live babies?**

F

H

G

J

5

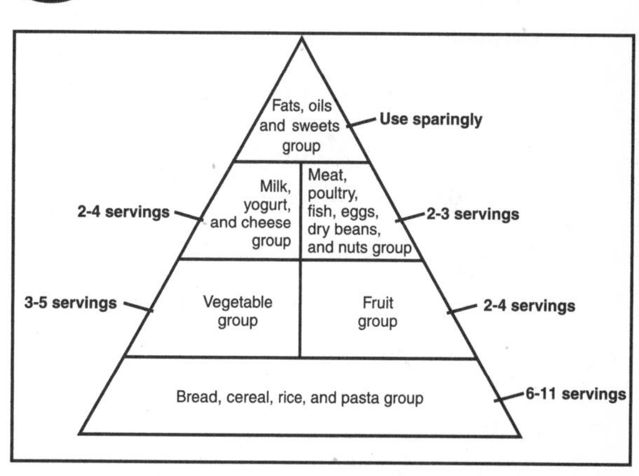

According to the Food Guide Pyramid, which of these foods should you eat most often?

A Peanuts

B Ham

C Bread

D Cheese

Stanford 9 • Unit Seven

Name: ______________________________ Date: ______________

6 **Which organ in the human body is responsible for holding and feeding a growing embryo?**

F Stomach

G Breast

H Ovary

J Uterus

7 **Which organ in the body is responsible for interpreting and sending messages to your body?**

A Heart

B Stomach

C Brain

D Skin

8 **Reflexes are actions like breathing, coughing, and keeping your balance. How are these actions similar to each other?**

F They are all things your lungs do.

G They are all things your body does automatically.

H They are all related to eating.

J They are all things children cannot do.

9

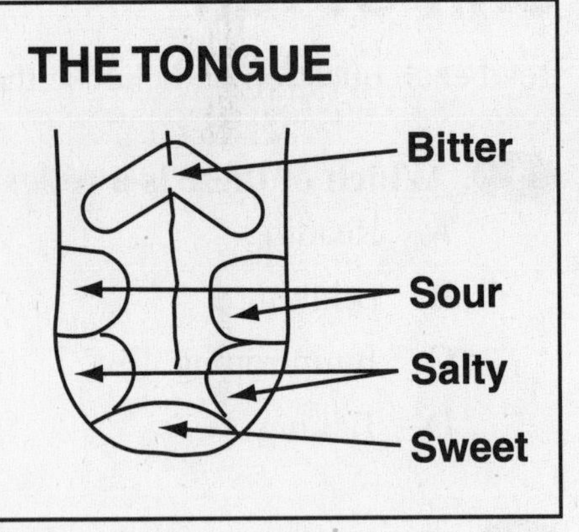

This picture shows where your different taste buds are located on your tongue. What would you predict would happen if you dropped a piece of sugar at the very tip of your tongue?

A It would taste bitter.

B It would taste salty.

C It would taste sweet.

D It would taste sour.

10 **Jennifer's science partner drops a ruler for her to catch. The first time she misses it. What do you predict will happen to her reaction time when she repeats the experiment twenty times?**

F Her reaction time will get faster with practice.

G Her reaction time will stay the same.

H Her reaction time will get slower with practice.

J Her brain will stop sending the message to her fingers to catch the ruler.

Name: ____________________ Date: __________

11 **When a person breaks his spinal cord in an accident, he might be —**

A unable to hear very well

B unable to move his legs anymore

C unable to see very well

D unable to remember things

12 **Doctors can use an electroencephalograph (EEG) to measure brain activity. Which of the following questions might be answered by using an EEG?**

F Does pulse change with exercise?

G What is the function of the liver?

H What parts of the brain are working while a person sleeps?

J Do cholesterol and high blood pressure cause heart attacks?

13 **The time in a woman's life when her ovaries stop releasing eggs each month is called —**

A menstruation

B menopause

C puberty

D childbirth

WHAT HAPPENS AFTER AN EGG IS FERTILIZED

Fertilized egg

2 cells

4 cells

8 cells

Many cells

The pictures show what happens once an egg is fertilized by a sperm. What phrase best describes what change is happening?

F The egg is making more sperm.

G The arms and legs of the embryo are being created.

H The fertilized egg is dividing many times to make more cells.

J The fertilized egg is becoming twins.

15 **A developing baby inside the mother's uterus is surrounded by —**

A air

B a fluid-filled sac

C a hard shell

D the mother's ribcage

Stanford 9 • Unit Seven

Name: ______________________________ Date: ______________

16 **Twins who are identical developed from one original egg and sperm. Twins who are not identical —**

F developed from one original egg and sperm as well

G are born in different years

H are always female

J developed from two different eggs and sperm

17 **In order to help the mother push the baby during childbirth, the walls of her uterus are made of —**

A strong muscle

B bone

C skin

D food

18 **Which of the following is a sexually transmitted disease?**

F Chicken pox

G AIDS

H Influenza

J Cancer

19 **For homework you are asked to learn the alphabet backwards. What might help you to do this?**

A Guessing

B Instinct

C Repetition

D Trial and error

20 **Which of the following is *not* a way that you could become more active during your day?**

F Taking the elevator rather than the stairs

G Riding your bike to school instead of the bus

H Going for a walk instead of watching TV

J Walking to the store rather than driving

Stanford 9

Answer Keys

Grade 6 Stanford 9 Answer Keys

Question Number	Correct Answer	Code/ Objective
Unit One		
1	C	Physical Science-03
2	J	Physical Science-01
3	A	Physical Science-01
4	H	Physical Science-03
5	B	Physical Science-01
6	J	Physical Science-03
7	C	Physical Science-01
8	J	Physical Science-01
9	A	Earth Science-03
10	G	Physical Science-02
11	D	Physical Science-02
12	F	Physical Science-03
13	D	Physical Science-01
14	H	Physical Science-02
15	B	Physical Science-03
16	H	Physical Science-02
17	B	Physical Science-03
18	J	Physical Science-01

Question Number	Correct Answer	Code/ Objective
Unit Two		
1	C	Life Science-03
2	H	Life Science-01
3	D	Life Science-01
4	H	Life Science-02
5	B	Life Science-02
6	G	Life Science-03
7	C	Life Science-03
8	J	Life Science-01
9	B	Life Science-01
10	F	Life Science-03
11	B	Life Science-02
12	H	Life Science-02
13	D	Life Science-03
14	G	Life Science-02
15	C	Life Science-01
16	G	Life Science-03
17	D	Life Science-01
18	J	Life Science-02
19	D	Life Science-02

Grade 6 Stanford 9 Answer Keys

Question Number	Correct Answer	Code/ Objective
Unit Three		
1	C	Physical Science-01
2	F	Physical Science-03
3	C	Physical Science-01
4	F	Physical Science-03
5	C	Physical Science-03
6	F	Physical Science-03
7	D	Earth Science-01
8	F	Physical Science-03
9	C	Physical Science-01
10	G	Physical Science-01
11	C	Physical Science-03
12	J	Earth Science-03
13	A	Physical Science-02
14	G	Physical Science-02
15	C	Physical Science-02
16	F	Physical Science-03
17	B	Physical Science-01
18	G	Earth Science-02
19	A	Physical Science-02
20	G	Physical Science-01

Question Number	Correct Answer	Code/ Objective
Unit Four		
1	B	Earth Science-02
2	G	Earth Science-03
3	B	Earth Science-03
4	F	Earth Science-02
5	C	Earth Science-01
6	G	Earth Science-03
7	A	Earth Science-03
8	H	Earth Science-02
9	D	Earth Science-01
10	G	Earth Science-02
11	A	Earth Science-02
12	H	Earth Science-01
13	D	Earth Science-02
14	H	Earth Science-03
15	A	Earth Science-03
16	G	Earth Science-02
17	C	Earth Science-02
18	G	Earth Science-02
19	D	Earth Science-01

Grade 6 Stanford 9 Answer Keys

Question Number	Correct Answer	Code/ Objective
Unit Five		
1	C	Earth Science-02
2	J	Earth Science-02
3	C	Earth Science-01
4	G	Earth Science-01
5	B	Earth Science-03
6	G	Earth Science-03
7	C	Earth Science-02
8	F	Earth Science-01
9	B	Earth Science-03
10	H	Earth Science-02
11	A	Earth Science-03
12	G	Earth Science-02
13	C	Earth Science-02
14	J	Earth Science-02
15	A	Earth Science-03
16	G	Earth Science-01
17	C	Earth Science-02
18	F	Earth Science-02
19	B	Earth Science-03
20	H	Earth Science-02

Question Number	Correct Answer	Code/ Objective
Unit Six		
1	B	Life Science-02
2	G	Life Science-01
3	A	Life Science-03
4	F	Life Science-01
5	B	Life Science-01
6	G	Life Science-01
7	B	Life Science-03
8	F	Life Science-03
9	C	Life Science-01
10	F	Physical Science-02
11	D	Physical Science-02
12	G	Life Science-01
13	A	Life Science-01
14	H	Life Science-02
15	D	Life Science-01
16	G	Life Science-02
17	C	Life Science-02
18	J	Life Science-02
19	B	Earth Science-02
20	H	Life Science-03

Grade 6 Stanford 9 Answer Keys

Question Number	Correct Answer	Code/ Objective
Unit Seven		
1	B	Life Science-03
2	J	Life Science-01
3	C	Life Science-01
4	G	Life Science-02
5	C	Life Science-01
6	J	Life Science-03
7	C	Life Science-03
8	G	Life Science-02
9	C	Life Science-01
10	F	Life Science-02
11	B	Life Science-03
12	H	Life Science-03
13	B	Life Science-03
14	H	Life Science-01
15	B	Life Science-03
16	J	Life Science-02
17	A	Life Science-03
18	G	Life Science-03
19	C	Life Science-02
20	F	Life Science-02

TerraNova

TerraNova

TerraNova

TerraNova

TerraNova

TerraNova

WHAT DO I NEED TO KNOW ABOUT THE TERRANOVA SCIENCE SECTION?

The TerraNova covers many other subjects besides science. Your students will probably also take the reading/language arts, mathematics, and social studies sections of the TerraNova. This workbook prepares your students for the types of *science* questions they will see on the TerraNova.

In the sixth grade, students usually take Level 16 of the TerraNova. (In some cases, they may take Level 15 or Level 17.) They must take the Complete Battery, Survey, or Multiple Assessments version in order to have a science section. Ask your school's test coordinator or principal to find out which version and level of the test your students will take.

The following times and numbers of items are based on Form A, but other forms vary only slightly.

- If students take Level 16 of the Complete Battery, they will see 40 science questions and have 40 minutes for the science section.
- If students take Level 16 of the Survey, they will see 25 science questions and have 25 minutes for the science section.
- If students take Level 16 of the Multiple Assessments, they will see 36 multiple-choice science questions and open-ended science questions, for which they will have 60 minutes. Most of the questions are multiple-choice.

The TerraNova is a norm-referenced test, which means that it can be used to compare one group of students to another. On each student's score report, there will be a percentile score that shows how she has performed compared to other students at the same grade level. However, technically, the student is not being compared to *all* students at that grade level across the country. She is only compared to the group of students that was in the norm group—a group that *represents* all students at that grade level across the country.

Because the TerraNova is a national test, its science questions are not based on any one state or district's science curriculum. This means that the TerraNova asks very general science questions. Students must understand general science concepts in order to do well, but they do not need to know many specific factual details.

The list of "objectives" on page 91 shows the broad areas of science knowledge that are covered on the TerraNova.

TerraNova Science Objectives for Grade 6

Each objective is followed by the code used in the answer key to indicate which questions in the unit tests are associated with it.

Science Inquiry (Science-19)

These questions test students' familiarity with the purposes and methods of scientific experiments. Students must also be able to interpret tables, graphs, and flow charts that show scientific data.

Physical Science (Science-20)

These questions test students' knowledge of physical properties and changes in those properties. They also test knowledge of force, motion, and energy.

Life Science (Science-21)

These questions ask students about organisms, their characteristics, and their interactions with each other.

Earth and Space Science (Science-22)

These questions ask students about the Sun, Earth, and Moon, and their relationships. They also ask students about Earth science topics, such as weather and geology.

Science and Technology (Science-23)

These questions test students' knowledge of science-related technology and natural versus human-made materials.

Personal and Social Perspectives in Science (Science-24)

These questions test students' ability to determine environmental changes and degradation, health issues, and safety issues. They also ask students to demonstrate an understanding of the effects of these changes and issues at a personal, community, and worldwide level.

History and Nature of Science (Science-25)

These questions are similar to those covering Science Inquiry. They require students to know about the general purposes and methods of scientific investigation.

WHAT DO MY STUDENTS NEED TO KNOW ABOUT THE TERRANOVA?

The following approaches can help students before the actual TerraNova administration.

Ease Students' Minds While Motivating Them

- Let students know that the TerraNova is not a test of how smart they are. It is a test that lets them show the skills and facts they have learned in class, and what they have yet to learn.
- Emphasize that the TerraNova will not affect students' grades, but that they should do their best because the test is important in a different way. It helps show what they've learned over this year and previous years.

Give Students the Facts About the Test

- Explain the difference between standardized tests and classroom tests. Point out the importance of each kind of test.
- Explain to students that they will probably come across some questions that are difficult for them to answer. They may even see a question that requires a skill or fact they have not learned at all. This test is designed to have some very difficult questions, so they should not get discouraged. All students will have trouble with some questions.
- Check to see which version and level of the TerraNova your students will take. Tell them how many science questions there will be and how much time they will have, according to the information on page 90. Let them know that there will also be math, language arts, and social studies questions in separate sections.
- Find out from the test coordinator at your school how many days your students will have to take all of the TerraNova sections. Reassure students that they will have more than one day to take the test.

Familiarize Students with the Testing Situation

- Remind students that standardized tests are not group activities, so they will have to work alone.
- If students are not used to using a separate answer sheet, be sure to explain this process and provide some practice using one in advance of the real test. The answer sheet on page 94 can help you do this.
- The TerraNova is a timed test, so students should work carefully and not allow themselves to get stuck on any one question. Working carefully but steadily, most students will be able to answer all or most of the questions.
- Try to determine which students feel anxious about the test and which are overconfident. Some students need to be reassured about their abilities, while others need to be made aware of careless errors they often make.

Provide Basic Test-taking Tips for the TerraNova

- ✔ Listen to all of the directions the teacher reads aloud.
- ✔ Read all directions in the test booklet carefully.
- ✔ Read each question and answer choice carefully. Always read all of the choices.
- ✔ Examine any graphics that accompany the question.
- ✔ Use your time wisely and don't get stuck on one question.
- ✔ Use the process of elimination. (See page 6 for one way to introduce the process of elimination to students in class.)
- ✔ Answer each question, even when you have not narrowed down the choices to just one.
- ✔ The TerraNova contains pictures and graphics that provide information that you can use to answer questions. Sometimes it's hard to tell whether a picture "goes with" a certain question. You should look for information that will help you in the picture on the page (and the pages before and after), but do not be alarmed if the pictures do not always help.

Provide Tips for Answering Questions with Graphics

Many questions in the TerraNova science section include graphics. We have included these types of questions in the unit tests so that students can practice the skills they will need to do well on the TerraNova.

The following types of graphics appear on the TerraNova:

- maps
- tables
- flow charts
- bar graphs
- pictures as answer choices (instead of words)
- sequenced pictures and text
- pictures showing various experimental situations
- pictures showing things to compare

Review maps, tables, flow charts, and bar graphs regularly with students to be sure they are familiar with how to interpret all of them. Be sure that they pay attention to the "fine print," like the titles, labels, and keys.

For any question involving a picture, instruct students to do the following:

1. Look closely at the details. You can get a lot of information from very small parts of the drawings on the TerraNova.
2. If there is more than one picture, think about the differences between them.
3. If there are words along with the pictures, read it all. Think about how it is related to the pictures.
4. Decide if there is any sort of order to the way the pictures and text are arranged. Are they in time order?
5. If you prefer to think in words, then name the things or organisms that you see before answering the question.
6. Sometimes more than one question is related to the same picture. Pay attention to the directions and other clues that help you see where to get information.

Name: ______________________ **Date:** __________

Unit Number: ______________________

1	Ⓐ	Ⓑ	Ⓒ	Ⓓ	14	Ⓕ	Ⓖ	Ⓗ	Ⓙ
2	Ⓕ	Ⓖ	Ⓗ	Ⓙ	15	Ⓐ	Ⓑ	Ⓒ	Ⓓ
3	Ⓐ	Ⓑ	Ⓒ	Ⓓ	16	Ⓕ	Ⓖ	Ⓗ	Ⓙ
4	Ⓕ	Ⓖ	Ⓗ	Ⓙ	17	Ⓐ	Ⓑ	Ⓒ	Ⓓ
5	Ⓐ	Ⓑ	Ⓒ	Ⓓ	18	Ⓕ	Ⓖ	Ⓗ	Ⓙ
6	Ⓕ	Ⓖ	Ⓗ	Ⓙ	19	Ⓐ	Ⓑ	Ⓒ	Ⓓ
7	Ⓐ	Ⓑ	Ⓒ	Ⓓ	20	Ⓕ	Ⓖ	Ⓗ	Ⓙ
8	Ⓕ	Ⓖ	Ⓗ	Ⓙ	21	Ⓐ	Ⓑ	Ⓒ	Ⓓ
9	Ⓐ	Ⓑ	Ⓒ	Ⓓ	22	Ⓕ	Ⓖ	Ⓗ	Ⓙ
10	Ⓕ	Ⓖ	Ⓗ	Ⓙ	23	Ⓐ	Ⓑ	Ⓒ	Ⓓ
11	Ⓐ	Ⓑ	Ⓒ	Ⓓ	24	Ⓕ	Ⓖ	Ⓗ	Ⓙ
12	Ⓕ	Ⓖ	Ⓗ	Ⓙ	25	Ⓐ	Ⓑ	Ⓒ	Ⓓ
13	Ⓐ	Ⓑ	Ⓒ	Ⓓ					

Name: ______________________ Date: ______________

Unit One

Directions

Read each question and choose the best answer. Mark your answer on your answer sheet.

1 Aaron and Tanja are investigating what happens to weight during an experiment. They have dropped a tablet into the test tube of water and quickly covered the test tube with the balloon. When the tablet in the test tube is finished dissolving, the scale should read

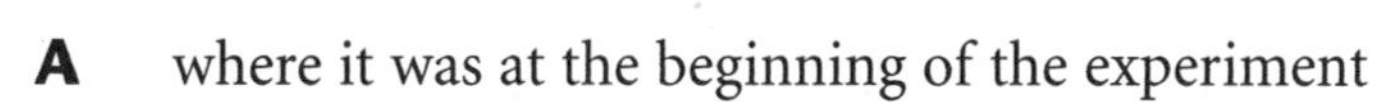

A where it was at the beginning of the experiment

B higher than at the beginning of the experiment

C lower than at the beginning of the experiment

D equal to zero

2 In this experiment, the balloon is there to

F collect the gas being made

G catch the water as it bubbles up

H make the experiment more interesting looking

J keep the scale at 0 g

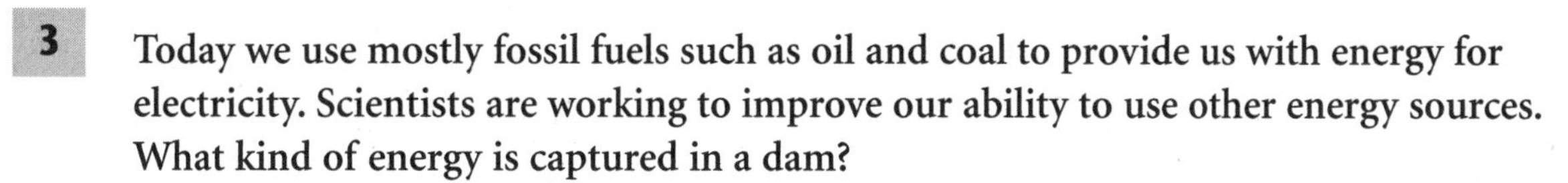

3 Today we use mostly fossil fuels such as oil and coal to provide us with energy for electricity. Scientists are working to improve our ability to use other energy sources. What kind of energy is captured in a dam?

A solar energy from the Sun

B fossil fuels

C nuclear energy from Earth's core

D potential energy from the stored water

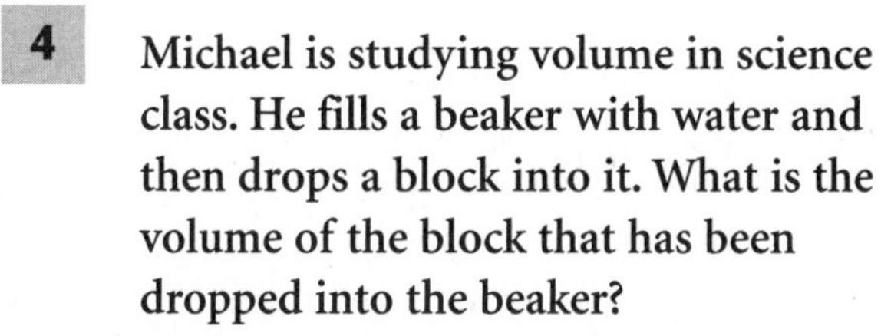

4 Michael is studying volume in science class. He fills a beaker with water and then drops a block into it. What is the volume of the block that has been dropped into the beaker?

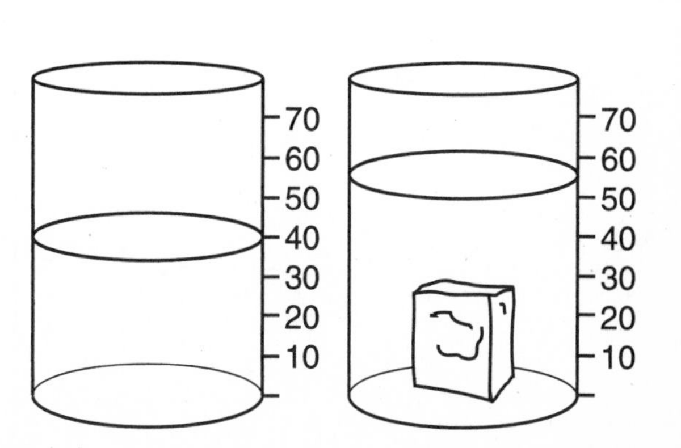

F 40 ml

G 55 ml

H 15 ml

J 25 ml

Name: ______________________ Date: ____________

5 A beaker of corn oil was put on one side of a balance and the same size beaker of water was put on the other side of the balance. What can be concluded about corn oil and water from looking at the picture?

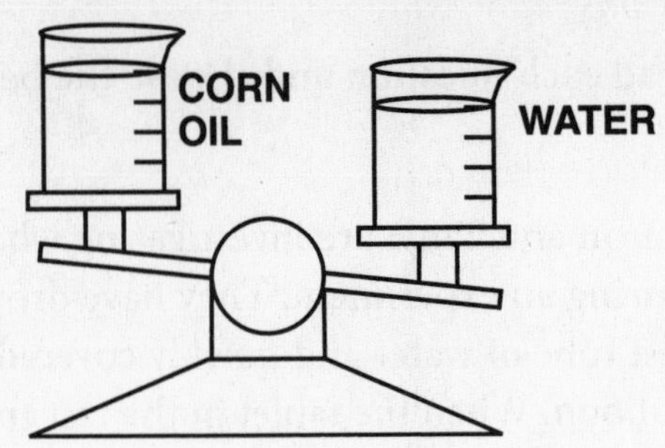

A Corn oil and water have the same density.

B Corn oil is more dense than water.

C Corn oil weighs more than water.

D Water is more dense than corn oil.

6 At room temperature, oxygen is a

F gas

G liquid

H solid

J solution

7 Chemists study physical and chemical changes. Which of the following is not a physical change?

A water boiling

B wood burning

C ice melting

D cutting cloth

8 Henry notices that when he is trying to float in the pool, he can float better if he takes a deep breath and holds it in. What is the most likely reason for this?

F Taking a deep breath pushes water away from you.

G Taking a deep breath makes a person more dense.

H Taking a deep breath makes a person weigh more.

J Taking a deep breath makes a person less dense.

9 Which of the following is not a metallic element?

A chlorine

B aluminum

C iron

D copper

Name: ______________________ Date: ____________

10 The picture shows what scientists thought was inside an atom one hundred years ago and what they think is inside an atom today. How has their thinking changed?

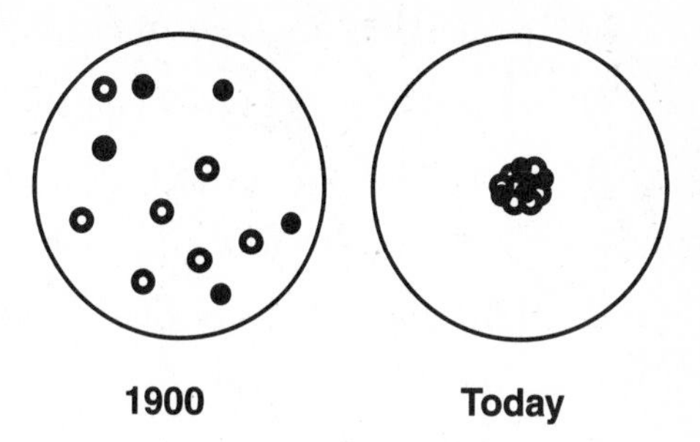

F Scientists used to think that the parts of an atom were all packed in the center, but now they think that they are spread all over the atom.

G Scientists used to think that atoms were empty, but now they think that they are full of smaller parts.

H Scientists used to think that the parts of atoms were lined up inside the atom, but now they think that they are packed in the middle of the atom.

J Scientists used to think the parts of an atom were spread all over the atom, but now they think that they are packed in the center of the atom.

11 Look at the picture showing solids, liquids, and gases. How is a gas different from a solid?

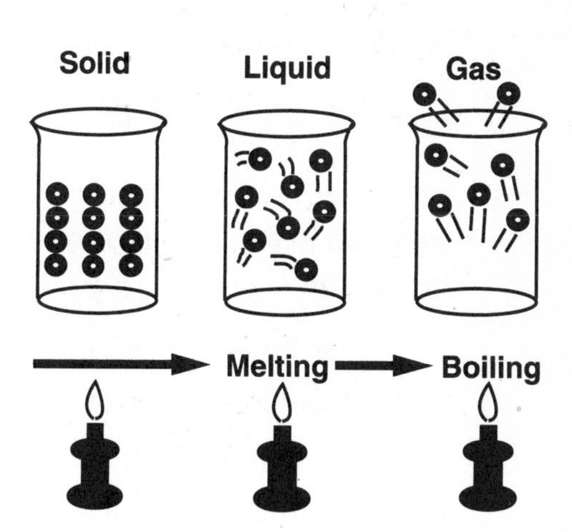

A Gas particles are packed tightly together, but solid particles move quickly.

B Solid particles move faster than gas particles.

C Solid particles are closer together than gas particles.

D Gas particles are colder than solid particles.

12 Joan is learning about acids and bases in science class. She is using litmus paper to test which substances are acids and which are bases. What will litmus paper do when it is dipped into a glass containing acid rain?

F turn blue

G turn red

H turn yellow

J turn green

Name: ______________________________ Date: ______________

13 **Marco designed this experiment for his school science fair. What is the most likely question his experiment is testing?**

A Does sand get hot when it is wet?

B Do sand and water heat up the same in the Sun?

C Do plants grow better in sand or in water?

D Do thermometers work better in sand or in mud?

14 **What is wrong with the way the above experiment is designed?**

F The water container should have more water in it.

G There shouldn't be any heat lamp.

H The heat lamp should be the same distance from the sand and water.

J There should be only one thermometer.

15 **Engineers use insulation for houses, picnic coolers, winter coats, and many other common items. What do scientists look for when creating a material to use as insulation?**

A something that is expensive

B something that is not a good conductor of heat

C something that lets heat escape through it

D something that melts easily

16 **A woman fills her car tires with air one cold winter day. What happens to the pressure in her car's tires when the season changes from winter to summer?**

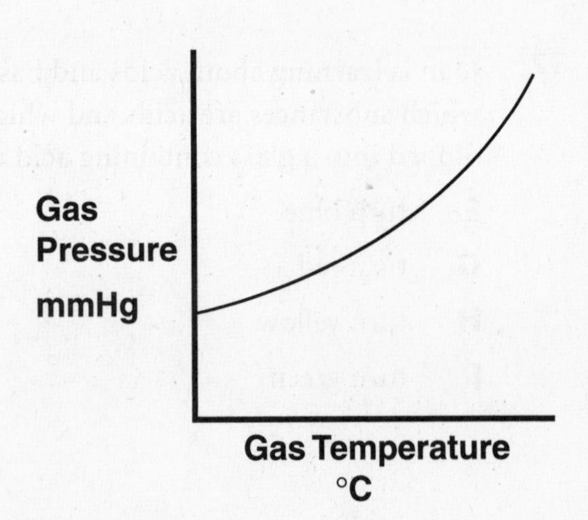

F The pressure of the air in the tires stays the same.

G The pressure of the air in the tires goes up.

H The pressure of the air in the tires goes down.

J The pressure of the air will make the tires deflate.

Name: ______________________ Date: ______________

Unit Two

Directions

Read each question and choose the best answer. Mark your answer on your answer sheet.

1 Andre's science class is learning about microorganisms found in pond water. Which piece of equipment should Andre use to look at microorganisms?

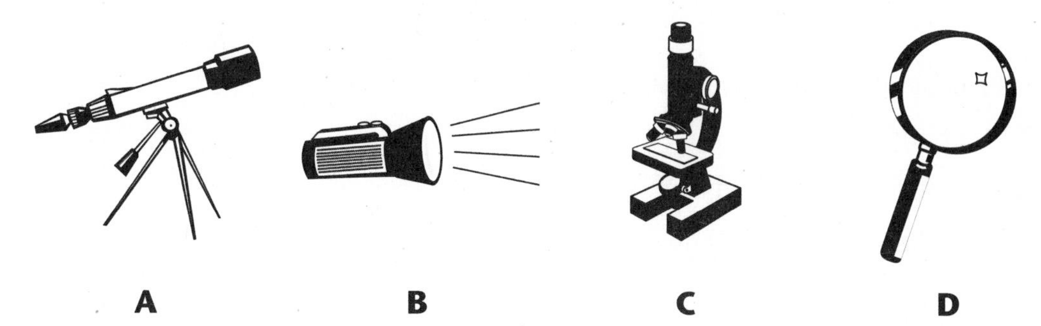

A **B** **C** **D**

2 Which of these is <u>not</u> found in any human cells?

F nucleus

G mitochondrion

H chloroplast

J cell membrane

3 A scientist performs research on how cell growth is controlled. Her findings might help to find a cure for

A AIDS

B baldness

C heart attacks

D cancer

4 Biologists have organized all living species into categories. Which statement explains what all the animals below have in common?

F All of these animals are amphibians.

G All of these animals are herbivores.

H All of these animals have bones.

J All of these animals lay eggs.

Name: ______________________ Date: ______________

5 During an autumn walk in the woods, Andy noticed the trees were losing their leaves. Walking in the same area the next summer, he noticed that most of the leaves that had fallen on the ground were gone. Which organisms are most likely responsible for this?

A carnivores

B herbivores

C omnivores

D decomposers

6 Which is not a characteristic that all living things share?

F ability to grow

G ability to make food from sunlight

H ability to reproduce

J ability to respond to the surroundings

7 What does Wendy need to add to her fish tank to make it a complete ecosystem that can survive without her help?

A birds

B fish

C water plants

D people

8 The chart shows the percentages of different elements that are present in your body. How much of your body is made up of oxygen and carbon?

F 65%

G 18.5%

H 28%

J 83.5%

ELEMENTS THAT MAKE UP THE HUMAN BODY

Symbol	Element	Percent
O	Oxygen	65.0
C	Carbon	18.5
H	Hydrogen	9.5
N	Nitrogen	3.3
Ca	Calcium	1.5
P	Phosphorous	1.0
K	Potassium	0.4
S	Sulfur	0.3
Na	Sodium	0.2
Cl	Chlorine	0.2
Mg	Magnesium	0.1

Name: ______________________ Date: ______________

9 Your body is a collection of millions of different cells. What percent of a human cell is not water?

A 70%

B 30%

C 15%

D 25%

CONTENTS OF A HUMAN CELL

Carbohydrates 1%
Water 70%
Proteins 15%
Lipids (fats) 10%
Nucleic acids 4%

10 Which invention allowed scientists to prove that all living things contain cells?

F the microscope

G the telescope

H the x-ray machine

J the computer

11 The cell membrane is the wall around the outside of every cell. There are materials floating around inside the cell and materials floating around in the fluid surrounding the cell. What does the picture tell you about the cell membrane?

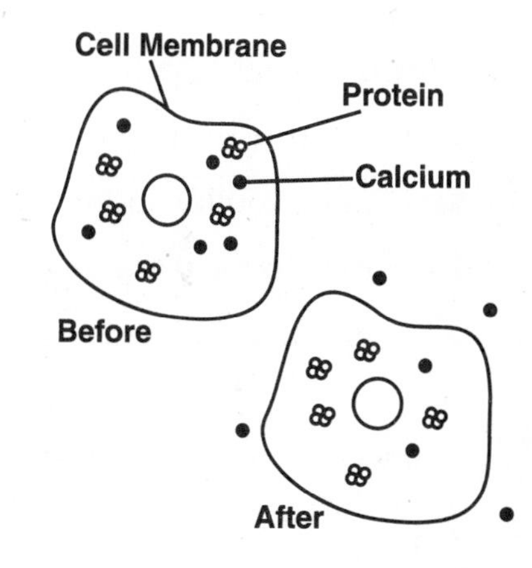

A It lets anything move across it.

B Calcium can diffuse across it, but protein cannot.

C It lets only large molecules diffuse across it.

D Protein can diffuse across it, but calcium cannot.

12 Oxygen is an important part of the daily function of both plants and animals. How do plants and animals use oxygen?

F Plants use oxygen during photosynthesis and animals make oxygen during respiration.

G Plants make oxygen during respiration and animals use oxygen during photosynthesis.

H Plants make oxygen during photosynthesis and animals use oxygen during respiration.

J Plants use oxygen during respiration and animals make oxygen during photosynthesis.

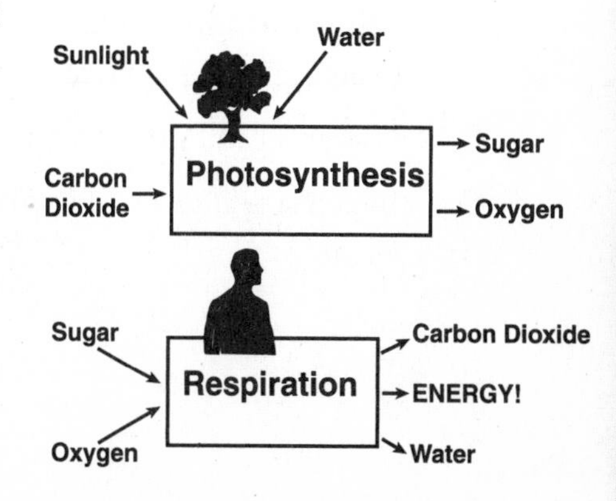

Name: ______________________ Date: __________

13 Which of the following is a fungus?

A pine tree

B amoeba

C clam

D mushroom

14 What do all members of the plant kingdom have in common?

F All plants are herbivores.

G All plants make their own food.

H All plants move from one place to another.

J All plants are vertebrates.

15 What word should go in the empty space in the table?

A fins

B shells

C body hair

D milk

ANIMALS WITH BACKBONES	
Animal Class	**Outer Covering**
Birds	Feathers
Reptiles	Dry Scales
Fish	Wet Scales
Mammals	

16 Why do tomato plants produce seeds inside the tomato?

F to make the tomato taste better

G to reproduce and make more tomato plants

H to help the plant make food from the Sun

J to make the tomatoes grow faster

17 A science class performs an experiment to test what keeps bacteria from growing in apple juice. They did different things to containers of apple juice and then checked them three days later. What can be concluded from the results?

A Boiling keeps bacteria from growing, but freezing doesn't.

B Salt is the only way to keep bacteria from growing in apple juice.

C Bacteria can't grow in apple juice.

D Bacteria will grow in apple juice if it is left alone.

	Apple Juice	Apple Juice	Apple Juice	Apple Juice
What was done:	Boiled then covered	Frozen	Salt added then covered	Left on window in science room
What happened:	Juice is still clear	Juice is still clear	Juice is still clear	Juice is cloudy with bacteria

Name: ______________________________ Date: ______________

Unit Three

Directions

Read each question and choose the best answer. Mark your answer on your answer sheet.

1 Jan, Mitch, Ellisa, and Corey are racing each other. The graph shows how far they each got after 10 seconds. Which runner was traveling at the highest speed?

A Jan

B Mitch

C Ellisa

D Corey

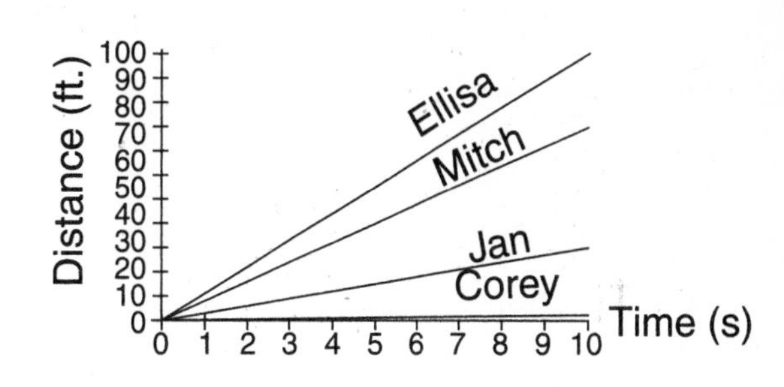

2 Which runner ran at a constant speed?

F Jan

G Mitch

H Ellisa

J Corey

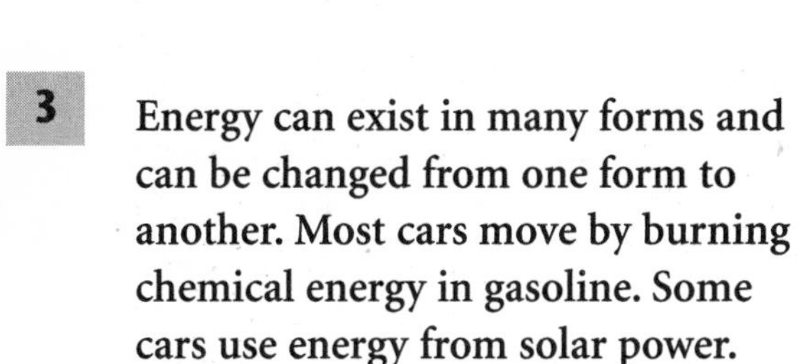

3 Energy can exist in many forms and can be changed from one form to another. Most cars move by burning chemical energy in gasoline. Some cars use energy from solar power. What kind of energy change occurs to make a solar-powered car run?

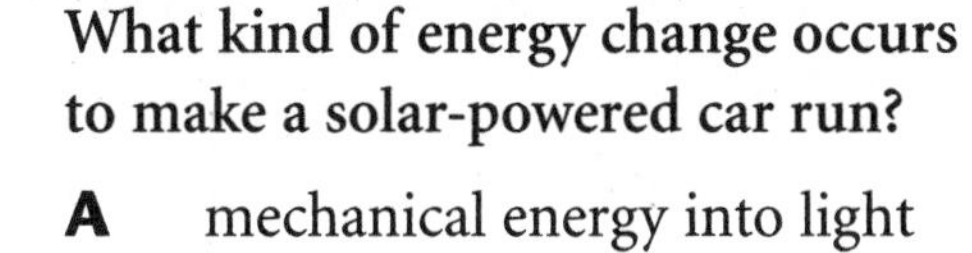

A mechanical energy into light energy

B heat energy into sound energy

C light energy into mechanical energy

D electrical energy into potential energy

4 Which surface would exert the least frictional force on your feet as you walk?

F ice

G rug

H sidewalk

J grass

5 Many car accidents occur because cars are traveling too quickly to make it safely around a turn. Inertia causes a car and its passengers to continue straight rather than follow the turn. Which technological improvements in cars help to keep people safe in their seats around curves?

A headlights

B mufflers

C windshields

D seat belts

Name: ____________________ Date: ____________

6 Jan parks in the parking lot of the city park and walks to the playground. Which direction is she walking?

F north

G south

H east

J west

47th Street
Entrance
Pond
City Park
Parking Lot
Playground
N W E S

7 When a car's speed increases, it is called

A acceleration

B position

C gravity

D friction

Slope of ramp (in degrees)	Distance ball rolls (in cm)
45	105
35	84
25	62

8 Juan and Anita are looking at how ramps affect rolling balls. What can be concluded about balls rolling down ramps from this experiment?

F The steeper the slope, the shorter the distance the ball rolls.

G The heavier the ball, the shorter the distance the ball rolls.

H The steeper the slope, the further the distance the ball rolls.

J The steepness of the slope doesn't affect how far the ball rolls.

9 What would be the most likely distance the ball would roll after going down a ramp with a 15-degree slope?

A 0 cm

B 45 cm

C 95 cm

D 125 cm

Name: ______________________ Date: ____________

10 Engineers designed bicycle brakes to slow the bicycle down when the brakes rub against the wheel. What kind of force is being applied to the wheel by the brakes?

F acceleration

G centripetal

H friction

J potential

11 When a ball is thrown up into the air, what makes it come back down again?

A air pressure

B wind

C speed

D gravity

12 Scientists have tried to design airplanes so that they move through the air as easily as possible. They design boats so that they move through water as easily as possible. What kind of force causes airplanes and boats to slow down as they move forward?

F drag force

G weight

H balanced force

J Newton

13 The heavier a moving object is, the more momentum it has. Which object has the most momentum?

A a bike going 5 miles per hour

B a school bus going 5 miles per hour

C a person running 5 miles per hour

D a small car going 5 miles per hour

14 Which object has the most kinetic energy?

F a bowling ball rolling 5 ft/s

G a golf ball rolling 5 ft/s

H a bowling ball rolling 20 ft/s

J a golf ball rolling 20 ft/s

15 How do batteries make a radio work?

A The battery has stored energy in it that can be changed into electricity.

B The battery has stored sounds in it that come out of the radio speakers.

C The battery takes energy from the radio to make it work.

D The chemicals move from the battery into the radio to make sound.

16 When Mary lets go of her pendulum, what will happen when the pendulum swings back toward her?

F The ball will go higher and higher with each swing.

G The ball will not go as high after each swing.

H The ball will go back to the same height after each swing.

J The ball will stop after one swing.

Name: ______________________________ Date: ______________

17 Many countries use coal, natural gas, and oil as sources of energy for motor vehicles and electricity. What does it mean to conserve these natural sources of energy?

A to sell as much of them as possible

B to use as little as necessary because they might run out

C to trade them with other countries around the world

D to try to discover more of these energy sources in the ground

18 What do all of these simple machines have in common?

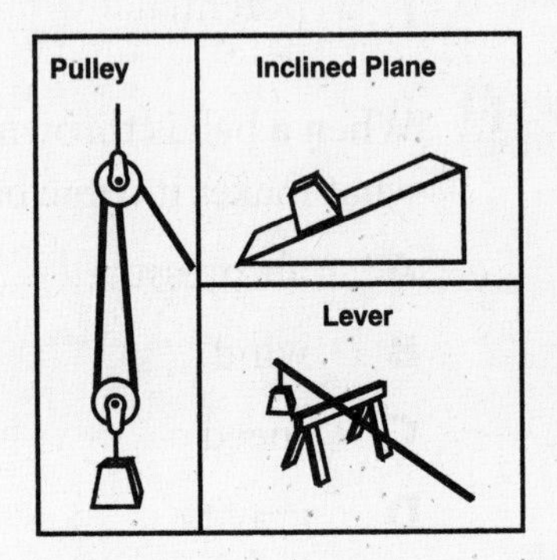

F They all make it easier to do work.

G They all make it harder to do work.

H They all work without any friction.

J They all have many parts.

19 When Sean pulls down on the pulley rope, what will happen?

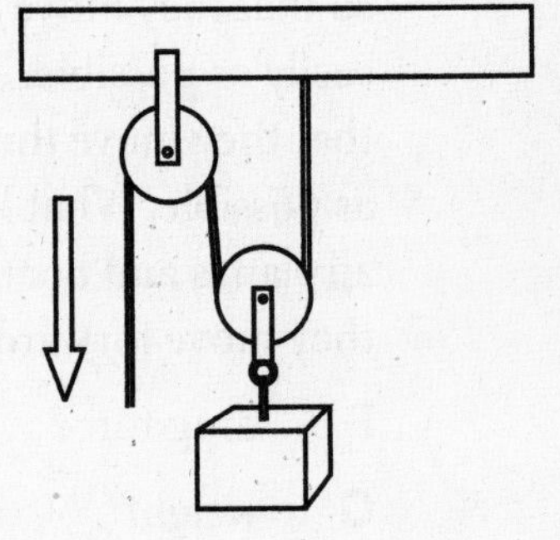

A The block will go down.

B The block will go up.

C The block will not move.

D The block will move to the left.

Name: ______________________ Date: ____________

Unit Four

Directions

Read each question and choose the best answer. Mark your answer on your answer sheet.

1 Scientists working at NASA have had to use technology to find ways for spaceships to carry everything astronauts will need while traveling in space. Which would be least important to bring with you into space?

A carbon dioxide
B oxygen
C food
D water

2 Bridget's science class is walking through Central Park in New York. They are investigating where the sun is in the sky at different times of day. It is 5:00 PM and the Sun is warming Bridget's back as she walks, so she must be traveling

F north
G south
H east
J west

3 Which of these gives off its own light?

A Saturn
B star
C comet
D Jupiter

4 Instead of moving in a straight line, Earth orbits the Sun. What causes this?

F gravity of the Sun
G inertia
H the other planets
J the Moon

5 Which instrument would be most useful for learning more about the planet Mars?

A microscope
B telescope
C magnifying glass
D x-ray machine

6 When NASA wants to send astronauts into space to do experiments and then bring them back when the experiments are done, they use a

F space shuttle
G star
H satellite
J missle

Name: ______________________ Date: ____________

7 When engineers design spacecraft, they make sure that water used by the astronauts can be purified and reused inside the spacecraft. Why do they need to recycle water in a spacecraft?

A because they can collect water from outer space

B because they need water to power the spacecraft

C because they can only bring small amounts of water with them

D because they need to breathe water vapor

Use the table below to answer questions 8 and 9.

PAST SPACE MISSIONS			
Year	Spacecraft	Carrying Crew?	Mission
1958	Explorer III	No	Discovered Earth's radiation belt
1966	Surveyor I	No	First American soft landing on Moon's surface
1969	Apollo 11	Yes	First landing by humans on the Moon
1972	Pioneer 10	No	Flew by and took pictures of Jupiter
1990	Hubble Space Telescope	No	Took pictures of stars and collision of comet with Jupiter
1996	Mars Pathfinder	No	Sent remote controlled car to take pictures of surface of Mars

8 When did humans first land on the moon?

F 1958

G 1966

H 1969

J 1996

9 Why was the Hubble Space Telescope sent into space?

A to land on the Moon

B to land on Mars and take pictures

C to fly by Jupiter

D to take pictures of stars and planets

10 If you are walking and your shadow is stretched out in front of you, where is the Sun?

F in front of you

G behind you

H on your left side

J directly overhead

Name: ______________________ Date: ______________

11 Hanna is studying how shadows are made by the sun. She sets her paper and a pencil up on the sidewalk outside her house early one morning. Which picture shows the correct shadow pattern made by her pencil at sunrise?

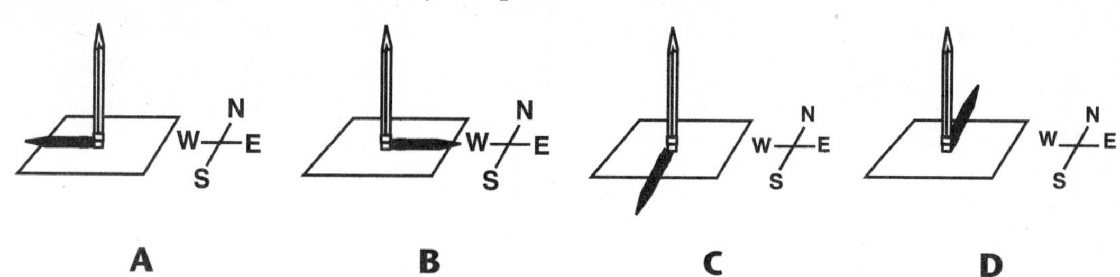

12 If it is 6:00PM in Miami, FL, what time is it in San Francisco, CA?

F 9:00 PM

G 3:00 AM

H 3:00 PM

J 4:00 PM

Some U.S. Time Zones

Boston, MA
Green Bay, WI
PST
MST
CST
EST
San Francisco CA
Charlotte, NC
Phoenix, Az
Houston, TX
Miami, FL
PST MST CST EST

13 Which of the following cities sees the sunrise first each day?

A San Francisco, CA

B Phoenix, AZ

C Green Bay, WI

D Boston, MA

14 Which part of the water cycle uses the Sun as a source of energy to make it happen?

F runoff

G infiltration

H evaporation

J precipitation

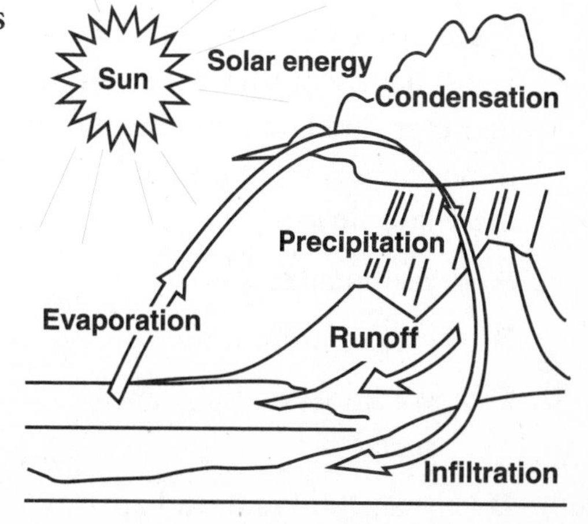

Name: ______________________________ Date: ______________

15 The gravity of the Moon and the Sun pull on Earth's oceans, making them rise and fall along the shore. This is called

A the tides

B an eclipse

C precipitation

D the seasons

16 Marty's science homework for the month of January is to look up at the night sky and draw what he sees. His observations for January 10 and January 20 are shown here. He notices that one light has moved between those two dates. What was the light marked "A" most likely?

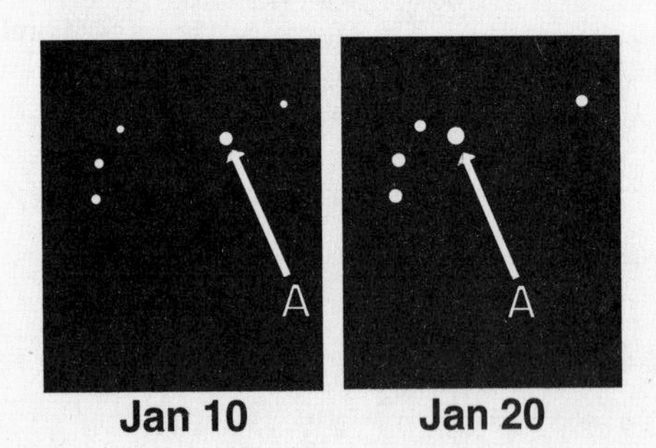

F an airplane

G a planet

H a space station

J a star

17 Space probes sent to Mercury and Venus have sent back information that there are lava flows on both of these planets. What probably caused these lava flows?

A earthquakes

B erosion from water

C volcanoes on the planets' surfaces

D space probes from Earth

18 Earth's atmosphere has lots of oxygen in it, but there is no oxygen in the atmospheres on Mercury, Venus, or Mars. Where did all of the oxygen in Earth's atmosphere probably come from?

F stars

G plants on Earth giving off oxygen during photosynthesis

H animals breathing out oxygen

J outer space

19 The alcohol in a thermometer expands and contracts when the temperature changes. What makes the alcohol rise?

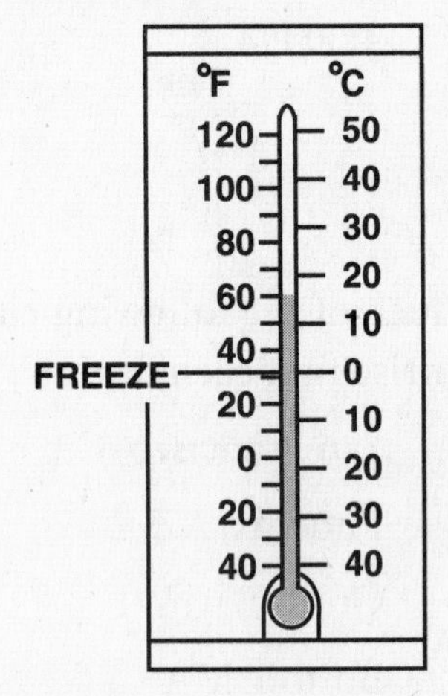

A When it gets colder, the alcohol expands and moves up the tube.

B When it gets warmer, the alcohol contracts and moves down the tube.

C When it gets colder, more alcohol comes into the tube from the air.

D When it gets warmer, the alcohol expands and moves up the tube.

Name: ______________________________ Date: ______________

Unit Five

Directions

Read each question and choose the best answer. Mark your answer on your answer sheet.

1 Geologists believe that Earth's continents were bunched together millions of years ago. Slowly, Earth's crust has moved, spreading the continents apart as they are today. According to this theory, which is the oldest picture of Earth?

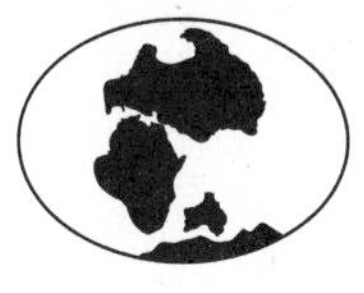

A **B** **C** **D**

2 Huge moving fields of ice are known as

F magma

G glaciers

H bedrock

J mantle

3 A geologist discovers an unusual looking fossil buried in a canyon wall made of sedimentary rock. Further along the wall she finds a second fossil in a different layer of the sedimentary rock. She can guess which fossil is older oldest because

A smaller fossils are always older

B the oldest layers of rock are always granite

C older fossils are always more damaged

D the fossil in a deeper layer of sedimentary rock is usually older

4 The Grand Canyon was created by

F earthquakes

G volcanoes

H a fault

J erosion by rivers

Name: ________________________________ Date: ______________

5 Soil forms over thousands of years. It starts with

A weathering of rock

B animals

C lava from volcanoes

D humus

6 Which of the following is an example of the Earth's crust moving?

F fossils

G hurricanes

H earthquakes

J waves

7 The picture shows a piece of the ocean floor around a deep sea vent. Which area of this ocean floor was made most recently?

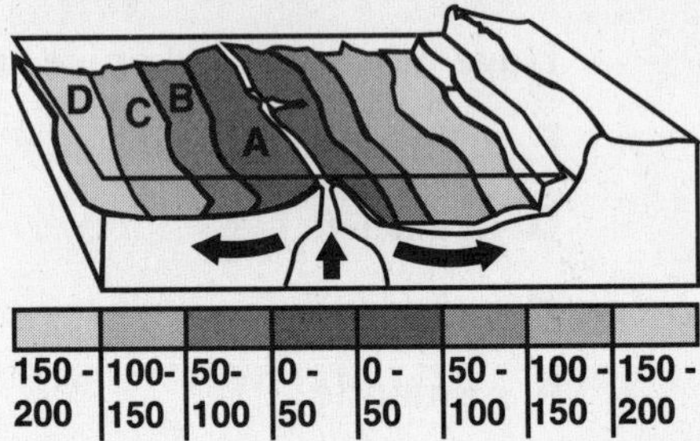

A area A

B area B

C area C

D area D

8 Which of the following is a natural resource that comes from Earth's crust?

F wood

G coal

H cloth

J rain

9 The west coast of Africa and the east coast of South America have matching shapes, almost like two fitting puzzle pieces. This suggests that

A there used to be no Atlantic Ocean

B they were eroded in the same way by the ocean

C they were once next to each other millions of years ago

D there are the same animals living in Africa and South America

Name: ______________________ Date: ____________

10 Which of the following was not present when dinosaurs roamed Earth?

F water

G volcanoes

H plants

J humans

11 Fossils usually are of shells, bones, or teeth because all of these parts-

A are hard and last long enough to be preserved

B are soft and decay quickly

C are found in every living thing

D were found in ancient animals, but not in animals living today

12 One problem farmers have had in recent years is that they are losing the soil from their fields. Which is not a technique to reduce soil erosion on farms?

F planting rows of trees to block the wind

G keeping the soil dry and loose

H planting strips of plants with deep roots

J planting grass on large dirt fields

13 When sedimentary rocks in the crust are exposed to heat and pressure, they can change into

A igneous rock

B sedimentary rock

C metamorphic rock

D plastic

14 Geologists divide minerals into different categories, depending on various characteristics of the minerals. Which is not a characteristic they use?

F by hardness

G by texture

H by structure

J by taste

15 The picture shows an experiment done in Martin's science class. What is he probably trying to find out?

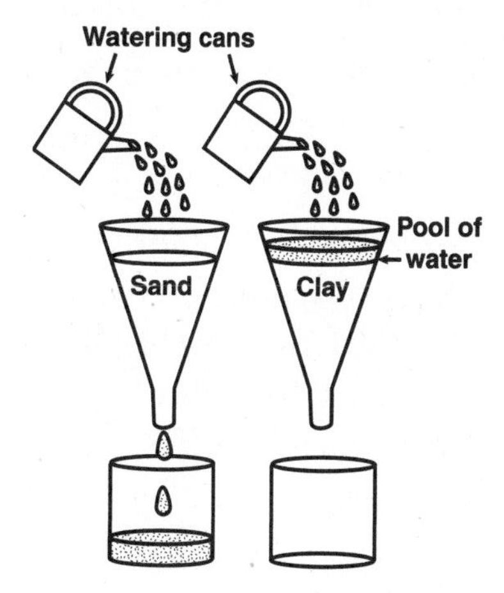

A whether water flows better through sand or clay

B which is the best kind of watering can

C which kind of soil seeds grow best in

D how much sand can fit in a funnel

Name: ______________________ Date: __________

16 If gravel was also going to be tested in this experiment, which funnel should be added to compare to the others?

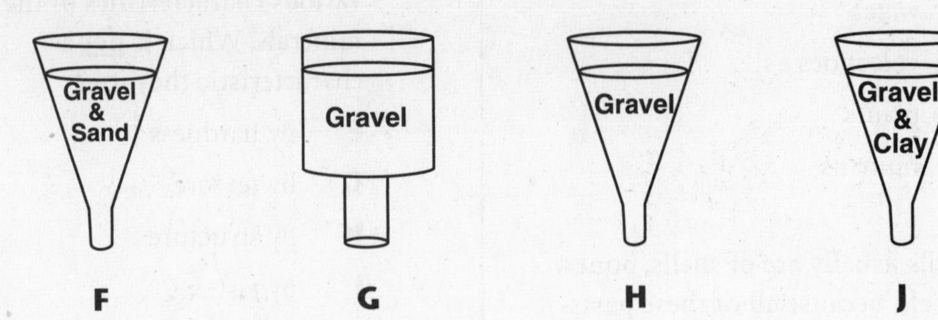

17 How could farmers use the results of this experiment to make their crops grow better?

A They could use the results to choose a soil that helps rain get to plant roots better.

B They could put lots of clay in their fields to let rain seep into the roots of their crops.

C They could grow their crops in mud.

D They could add fertilizers to their soil.

18 For homework, Julie is asked to fill a measuring cup with water and then leave it in the freezer overnight. What can be concluded from this experiment about water when it freezes?

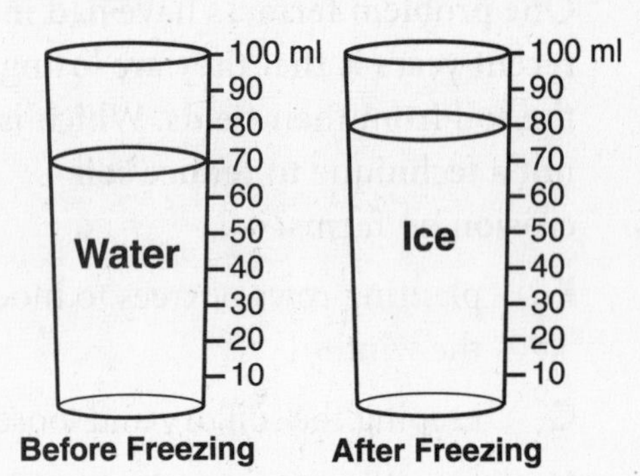

F Water changes into another liquid when it freezes.

G Water expands when it turns into ice.

H Water has a volume of 80 ml every time it freezes.

J Water contracts when it turns into ice.

19 How do geologists believe fold mountains are formed?

A Rock layers are squeezed together as Earth's crust moves.

B Fold mountains are inactive volcanoes.

C Rock layers are tilted and broken apart.

D Earthquakes cause large cracks in Earth's crust.

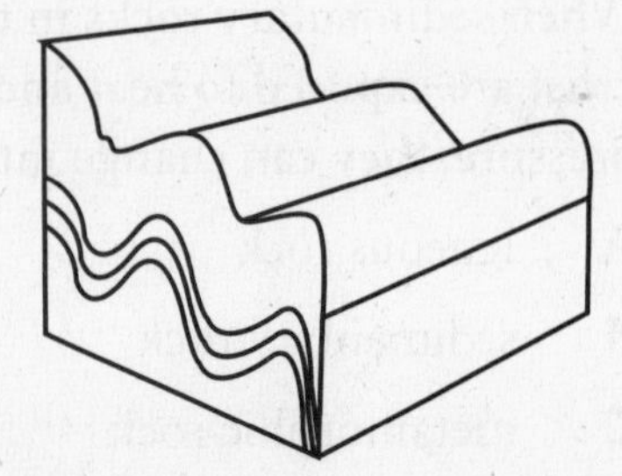

Name: ______________________ Date: ______________

Unit Six

Directions

Read each question and choose the best answer. Mark your answer on your answer sheet.

IF YOU ARE BLOOD TYPE	YOU CAN RECEIVE TYPE	YOU CAN DONATE TO PEOPLE WITH TYPE
A	O, A	A, AB
B	O, B	B, AB
AB	O, A, B, AB	AB
O	O	A, B, AB, O

1 Georgette is in the hospital and needs someone to donate blood to her. Her blood type is B. Which kind(s) of blood can she receive?

A A or O

B B or O

C only B

D B or AB

2 Several months later, Georgette donates blood at the hospital so that there is blood available when people need it. Georgette's blood could be given to people with blood type

F A or O

G B or O

H only B

J B or AB

3 Josh is studying heredity in science class. Heredity is when characteristics are passed on from parents to offspring. Which of these is a trait Josh inherited from his parents?

A where he lives

B his eye color

C his age

D his hair length

4 In 1997, scientists announced that they had created a sheep named Dolly who was a clone. The scientists had taken DNA from an adult sheep and used it to make Dolly. Because Dolly and the other sheep had the same DNA, they were identical. Many scientists are excited about cloning because

F there is a shortage of sheep around the world

G they might be able to clone human cells to replace damaged ones in patients

H they didn't know DNA carried inherited traits

J they want use cloning to make many new kinds of sheep

Name: ______________________ Date: ____________

5 Jamie's science class is growing pea plants. They move small cotton balls from one flower to the next, imitating the way bees move among flowers. Why are Jamie and his friends doing this?

A They are eating the peas.

B They are carrying pollen that fertilizes the flowers.

C They are drying off the flowers.

D They are helping the plants to photosynthesize.

6 When pollen from purple pea plant flowers is used to fertilize white pea plant flowers, all of the offspring plants have purple flowers. What kind of trait is purple flower color in peas?

F a dominant trait

G a recessive trait

H not an inherited trait

J an incompletely dominant trait

7 When purple and white pea plants are crossed, all of the offspring plants have purple flowers. What kinds of plants should Melinda's science class get when they cross a tall plant with a short plant?

	Seed Color	Flower Color	Plant Height
Dominant form	Yellow	Purple	Tall
Recessive form	Green	White	Short

A Half the offspring plants will be short and half will be tall.

B All of the offspring plants will be short.

C All of the offspring plants will be tall.

D Half of the offspring plants will be medium and half will be short or tall.

8 Peter fills a bag with 50 red jelly beans and 50 black jelly beans. If he reaches into the bag to pull out a jelly bean, what is the chance that he'll pull out a black one?

F 50%

G 1 out of 3

H 100%

J 1 out of 10

Name: ______________________ Date: ______________

9 Peter pulls out a jelly bean, records what color it is, and then puts it back into the bag. He repeats this 20 times. How many times did he probably get a red jelly bean?

A 20

B 1

C 0

D 9

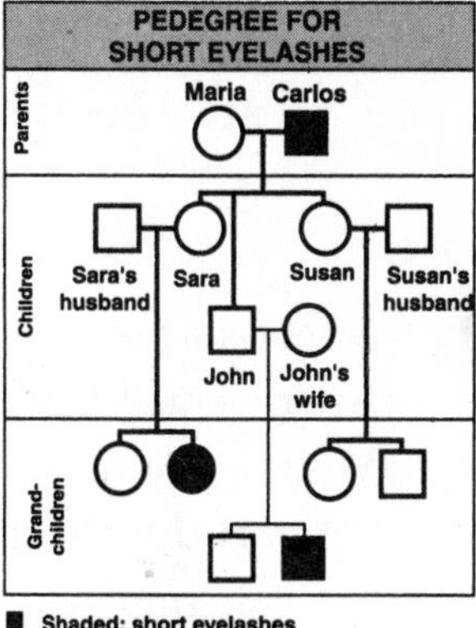

10 How many grandsons with long eyelashes do Maria and Carlos have?

F 1

G 2

H 0

J 3

11 Sara and her husband have

A one daughter with long eyelashes and one daughter with short eyelashes

B one son with long eyelashes and one son with short eyelashes

C one daughter with long eyelashes and one son with long eyelashes

D one son with long eyelashes and one daughter with long eyelashes

Directions

Use the information below to answer questions 12 and 13.

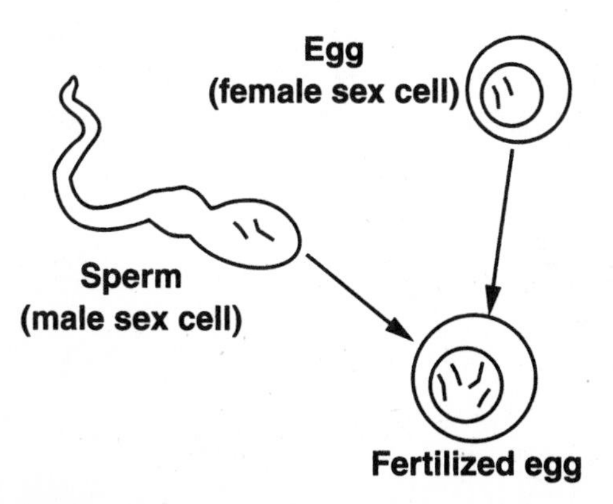

12 How does a fertilized egg get all of its chromosomes?

F all from the egg

G all from the sperm

H half from the egg and half from the sperm

J one quarter from the sperm and three quarters from the egg

13 What can be concluded from the chart about where a person's inherited traits come from?

A A person's traits are mostly from the father.

B A person's traits are mostly from the mother.

C A person doesn't inherit any traits.

D A person's traits are a mixture from the mother and father.

Name: ______________________________ Date: ______________

14 Many of a person's traits are inherited in her genes. A person's environment can also affect how she functions. Which of these is an example of an environmental affect?

F Judy has blue eyes like her mother and father.

G Mark was paralyzed in a car accident.

H Juan is as tall as his father.

J Mike has two dimples like his grandmother and sister.

15 Scientists believe that the woolly mammoth lived in North America more than a million years ago. What evidence do you think they have to support this theory?

A books written back then

B science fiction movies about woolly mammoths

C fossils of woolly mammoth bones and tusks

D pictures scientists found

16 Scientists at the American Museum of Natural History noticed that the labels have fallen off a display showing layers of fossils underground. Which of the labels should go on the bottom layer of fossils in the picture?

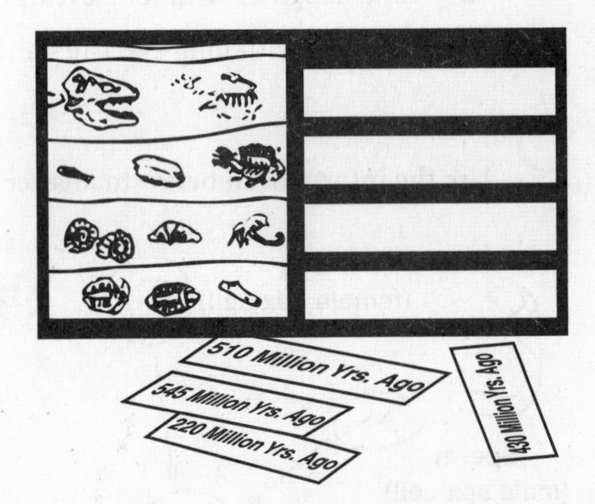

F 430 million years ago

G 545 million years ago

H 510 million years ago

J 220 million years ago

17 The bones in a bird's wing and a human's arm are similar in number and arrangement. This is evidence that

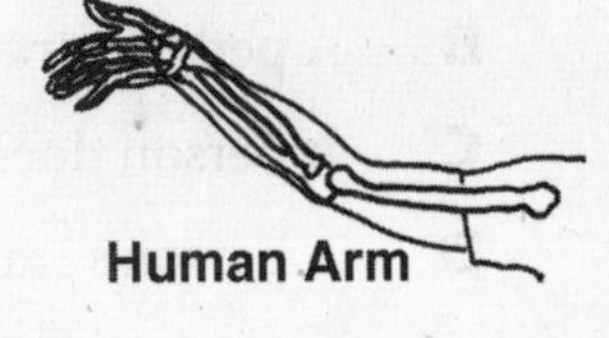

A humans and birds are the same species

B humans can fly

C birds are more intelligent than humans

D humans and birds evolved from a common ancestor

Name: ______________________ Date: ____________

Unit Seven

Directions

Read each question and choose the best answer. Mark your answer on your answer sheet.

Helen and three classmates perform an experiment to see the effect of exercise on pulse rate. They took their pulse while sitting down and then after doing jumping jacks.

Name	Pulse Before Exercise	Pulse After Exercise
Helen	60	88
John	55	90
Brianna	70	99
Peter	50	80

1 Which student's pulse was affected the most by exercise?

A Helen

B John

C Brianna

D Peter

2 Which of these is a reflex action?

F reading

G blinking

H jump-roping

J talking

3 Which of these is not one of your senses?

A smell

B sight

C thought

D hearing

4 Frank has diabetes, which means that his body can't make insulin. The gene that tells his body how to make insulin doesn't work. Scientists are working on technology that would allow them to repair or replace non-working genes. In Frank's case, he would need a new copy of the gene for

F making diabetes

G making blood

H making insulin

J making sugar

Name: ______________________________ Date: ______________

5 **Which organ in the human body is responsible for holding and feeding a growing embryo?**

A stomach

B breast

C ovary

D uterus

6 **Which organ in the body is responsible for interpreting and sending messages to your body?**

F heart

G stomach

H brain

J skin

7 **Reflexes are actions like breathing, coughing, and keeping your balance. How are these actions similar to each other?**

A They are all things your lungs do.

B They are all things your body does automatically.

C They are all related to eating.

D They are all things children cannot do.

8 **Nekesa and her partner are studying the sense of taste. This picture shows where your different taste buds are located on your tongue. What would you predict would happen when Nekesa drops a piece of sugar at the very tip of her partner's tongue?**

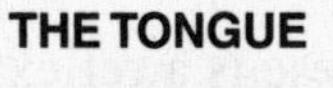

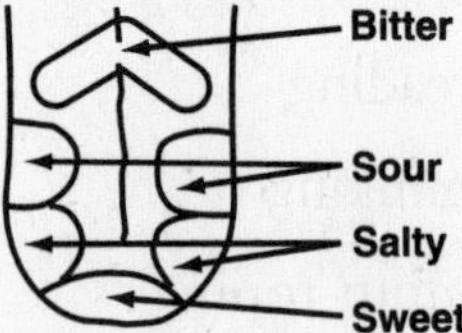

F Her partner will taste something bitter.

G Her partner will taste something salty.

H Her partner will taste something sweet.

J Her partner will taste something sour.

9 **Jennifer's science partner drops a ruler for her to catch. The first time she misses it. What do you predict will happen to her reaction time when she repeats the experiment twenty times?**

A Her reaction time will get faster with practice.

B Her reaction time will stay the same.

C Her reaction time will get slower with practice.

D Her brain will stop sending the message to her fingers to catch the ruler.

10 When a person breaks his spinal cord in an accident, he might be

- **F** unable to hear very well
- **G** unable to move his legs anymore
- **H** unable to see very well
- **J** unable to remember things

11 Doctors can use an electroencephalograph (EEG) to measure brain activity. Which of the following questions might be answered by using an EEG?

- **A** Does pulse change with exercise?
- **B** What is the function of the liver?
- **C** What parts of the brain are working while a person sleeps?
- **D** Does cholesterol cause heart attacks?

12 The time in a woman's life when her ovaries stop releasing eggs each month is called

- **F** menstruation
- **G** menopause
- **H** puberty
- **J** childbirth

13 The pictures show what happens once an egg is fertilized by a sperm. What phrase best describes what change is happening?

WHAT HAPPENS AFTER AN EGG IS FERTILIZED

Fertilized egg
2 cells
4 cells
8 cells
Many cells

- **A** The egg is making more sperm.
- **B** The arms and legs of the embryo are being created.
- **C** The fertilized egg is dividing many times to make more cells.
- **D** The fertilized egg is becoming twins.

14 A developing baby inside the mother's uterus is surrounded by

- **F** air
- **G** liquid
- **H** a hard shell
- **J** the mother's ribcage

Name: ______________________________ Date: ______________

15 Twins who are identical developed from one original egg and sperm. Twins who are not identical

A developed from one original egg and sperm as well
B are born in different years
C are always female
D developed from two different eggs and sperm

16 In order to help with childbirth, the walls of the mother's uterus are made of

F strong muscle
G bone
H skin
J food

17 Which of the following is a sexually transmitted disease?

A chicken pox
B AIDS
C influenza
D cancer

18 For homework, you are asked to learn the alphabet backwards. What might help you to do this?

F guessing
G instinct
H repetition
J trial and error

19 Which of the following is not a way that you could become more active during your day?

A taking the elevator rather than the stairs
B riding your bike to school instead of the bus
C going for a walk instead of watching TV
D walking to the store rather than driving

TerraNova

Answer Keys

Grade 6 TerraNova Answer Keys

Question Number	Correct Answer	Code/ Objective
Unit One		
1	A	Science-20
2	F	Science-19
3	D	Science-24
4	H	Science-19
5	D	Science-20
6	F	Science-20
7	B	Science-20
8	J	Science-20
9	A	Science-20
10	J	Science-25
11	C	Science-19
12	G	Science-20
13	B	Science-19
14	H	Science-19
15	B	Science-23
16	G	Science-23

Question Number	Correct Answer	Code/ Objective
Unit Two		
1	C	Science-23
2	H	Science-21
3	D	Science-24
4	H	Science-21
5	D	Science-21
6	G	Science-21
7	C	Science-19
8	J	Science-19
9	B	Science-24
10	F	Science-23
11	B	Science-21
12	H	Science-21
13	D	Science-21
14	G	Science-21
15	C	Science-21
16	G	Science-21
17	D	Science-19

Grade 6 TerraNova Answer Keys

Question Number	Correct Answer	Code/ Objective
Unit Three		
1	C	Science-19
2	H	Science-19
3	C	Science-23
4	F	Science-20
5	D	Science-23
6	J	Science-24
7	A	Science-20
8	H	Science-19
9	B	Science-19
10	H	Science-23
11	D	Science-20
12	F	Science-23
13	B	Science-20
14	H	Science-20
15	A	Science-23
16	G	Science-19
17	B	Science-24
18	F	Science-20
19	B	Science-19

Question Number	Correct Answer	Code/ Objective
Unit Four		
1	A	Science-23
2	H	Science-19
3	B	Science-22
4	F	Science-22
5	B	Science-23
6	F	Science-23
7	C	Science-23
8	H	Science-25
9	D	Science-25
10	G	Science-22
11	A	Science-19
12	H	Science-24
13	D	Science-24
14	H	Science-22
15	A	Science-22
16	G	Science-19
17	C	Science-22
18	G	Science-22
19	D	Science-23

Grade 6 TerraNova Answer Keys

Question Number	Correct Answer	Code/ Objective
Unit Five		
1	C	Science-25
2	G	Science-22
3	D	Science-19
4	J	Science-22
5	A	Science-22
6	H	Science-22
7	A	Science-19
8	G	Science-22
9	C	Science-22
10	J	Science-22
11	A	Science-22
12	G	Science-24
13	C	Science-22
14	J	Science-22
15	A	Science-19
16	H	Science-19
17	A	Science-24
18	G	Science-19
19	A	Science-22

Question Number	Correct Answer	Code/ Objective
Unit Six		
1	B	Science-19
2	J	Science-19
3	B	Science-21
4	G	Science-23
5	B	Science-19
6	F	Science-21
7	C	Science-19
8	F	Science-19
9	D	Science-19
10	G	Science-24
11	A	Science-24
12	H	Science-21
13	D	Science-21
14	G	Science-21
15	C	Science-22
16	G	Science-22
17	D	Science-21

Grade 6 TerraNova Answer Keys

Question Number	Correct Answer	Code/ Objective
Unit Seven		
1	B	Science-19
2	G	Science-21
3	C	Science-21
4	H	Science-23
5	D	Science-21
6	H	Science-21
7	B	Science-21
8	H	Science-19
9	A	Science-19
10	G	Science-21
11	C	Science-23
12	G	Science-21
13	C	Science-19
14	G	Science-21
15	D	Science-21
16	F	Science-21
17	B	Science-24
18	H	Science-24
19	A	Science-24